THE BRIDP

POETRY, SHORT ST(

JUDGES
Roger Robinson • Poetry
Colin Barrett • Short Stories
Christopher Allen • Flash Fiction

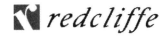

First published in 2023 by Redcliffe Press Ltd
81g Pembroke Road, Bristol BS8 3EA
e: info@redcliffepress.co.uk
www.redcliffepress.co.uk

Follow us on Twitter @RedcliffePress
© the contributors

Follow The Bridport Prize:
Follow us on Twitter and Instagram @BridportPrize

www.bridportprize.org.uk
www.facebook.com/bridportprize

ISBN 978-1-915670-11-3

Typeset in 10.5pt Times

Typeset by Addison Print Ltd, Northampton
Printed by Hobbs the Printers Ltd, Totton

Contents

Beacons of Light

Everyone has a story. Within these pages are short stories, poems and flash fiction by storytellers from across the world, beacons of light that steered us towards a creative shore we never knew existed then never wanted to leave.

We celebrate the writers within these pages who crafted their pieces alongside the endless demands of life, working late at night, early in the morning and whenever a precious moment could be snatched from the jaws of 'when I've done this'.

Whilst there is unbridled joy in being chosen as a winner, it's important to acknowledge those who didn't make it to the home strait. Every successful writer has ploughed the rejection field and experienced pain but simply knowing that can help the healing. Then, when you are ready and because writing really is as fundamental as breathing (you just can't stop yourself), start over.

Stories connect us. Our privilege and pleasure is to read new writers and discover unheard voices. This anthology overflows with original talent and extraordinary imagination. Thank you to all our winners and everyone who entered our competition. Without you, there are fewer stories in the world. Without stories, we are all adrift.

The Bridport Prize Team

Where are they now?

Freya Bantiff
Last year's joint winner of our Young Writer Award with her poem *Working Debenhams' Late Shift,* Freya went onto secure third place in the National Poetry Competition and was Canterbury Poet of the Year. Recently joint Apprentice Poet in Residence at Ilkley Literature Festival, Freya is studying for a Poetry MA at the University of East Anglia.

Jelle Cauwenburghs and Goldie Goldbloom
Two of our placed flash fiction winners from last year have featured in the Best Small Fictions anthology. Included were Jelle's *Yesterday They Crossed The Elbe* and Goldie's *In the Museums of Heaven and Hell.*

Rachael Fulton
Rachael's short story *Call* was highly commended in 2020 and therefore eligible for a prize not open to the general public – the Sunday Times/Audible Short Story Award. It was the richest prize for a single short story in the English language giving £30,000 to the winner. Rachael made the final shortlist. She went on to have another short work *Every Second Counts* read on Radio 4 and recently launched the podcast *Mums In The Making.*

Kexin Huang
Shortlisted for her poem *12.5mg, Freed* last year, Kexin's debut poetry pamphlet *Unlock* was published with Veer Books this summer. Kexin writes in three languages and her poems have been published in The Poetry Society, Modern Poetry in Translation and others.

Michael Lavers
Michael was our 2020 poetry winner. His collection *After Earth* was recently published by the University of Tampa Press to much acclaim. He lives in Provo, Utah, with his wife and two children and teaches Poetry at Brigham Young University.

Mark Pajak

Mark won our poetry award in 2016. His pamphlet *Spitting Distance* (Smithl Doorstop) was later selected by Carol Ann Duffy as a Laureate's Choice. *The Guardian* wrote of his recent debut *Slide* 'there is no fumbling beginner's luck, no rough moments or threadbare patches – its polished craftsmanship throughout is striking.'

David Swann

David has won with us the most notching up four short stories, four poems and three flash fiction successes. His novella *Season of Bright Sorrow* (Ad Hoc Press) has just been named international Rubery Book of the Year.

Hilary Taylor

After her flash fiction win last year with *Some Creatures Trapped in Ice,* Hilary's debut novel was published by Lightning Books. *Sea Defences* is set on the fragile Norfolk coast and Hilary already has a second novel in the works.

Lucy Weldon

Shortlisted for her short story in 2021, Lucy's debut collection *Ultra-marine* was published by Cinnamon Press this summer. Lucy takes inspiration from her time in countries across Europe, Asia and Australia. Born in Hong Kong, she is a published nonfiction author and worked as an international freelance journalist.

ROGER ROBINSON

Poetry Report

The importance of literary prizes, and in particular The Bridport Prize, is to connect readers with new and exciting writers. Appearing on the winners' list will guarantee new audiences for the writer, something particularly important during this time. I believe poetry and books have taken on added importance and are now regaining ground as an alternate technology as people tire of screens. I think it is safe to say that we all hope that trend continues and brings more audiences towards poetry.

What a privilege it has been to judge the Bridport Prize and to get to the heart of the poems received.

As the judge for the Bridport Prize, my task was to choose the best poems submitted to the prize. But what was the best poem? The one that I enjoyed the most, or the poem with the best craft? The poem that spoke to the future but gave a nod to the past? Was it the most politically strident or a poem that spoke to the turbulent times in which we all now live? The wildcard showing unrelenting promise? Or maybe all of the above?

The more I read, the more it became important that poems chosen for each stage challenge literary forms and norms. A sense of craft definitely played a part in my choices, but also how much the poem mattered. Did it take on new, big, or important themes that could resonate with readers years after its release? Of course, this is all subjective, but these contexts really helped me to move forward and helped guide my contribution to choosing the eventual winners. Letting new and fresh visions of reality lead the way, I chose the winners based on what I believed to be the best poems pushing at the edges of their forms in interesting ways, without sacrificing narrative or execution. I hope new readers will enjoy these poems as much as I have.

I would personally like to congratulate all the winners and highly commended poets and extend my thanks to The Bridport Prize and everyone involved for their support of writers and readers. The Bridport Prize is such an essential beacon for new writers and world literatures, so I would like to give a large round of applause for their relentless contributions to literature.

I've had the privilege of living with the poems for an extended time and am grateful for all of the work. Unfortunately, I could only choose a few poems, and it was an incredibly hard task, but I got there eventually. I want to talk about the ten highly commended poems that I have chosen for this year.

'The Sadness is on Me' is as close to the Spanish idea of Duende that Gaelic can get. A poem that quantifies its loss by contextually inferring what is lost.

'Grandma's Book Of Receipts', a poem of food and the senses that surround it, holds the weight of memory for emigrants.

'Fear' explores how pervasive the emotion of fearfulness can be when it takes hold. In its list making of fears, it illustrates how anxieties can grow exponentially.

In 'What We Think about Tintoretto', a father and son talk about the sensuality of painting to avoid talking about life.

'Ursa Major' plots the points of stars as a type of fate determining portions of tragedy in a life, but also its expanse is soothing in tragedy's aftermath.

In 'Blasphemy Americana', the syncopation of jazz is used to comment on the maelstrom of American politics.

'Noodles, August, the Courtyard of New York-Presbyterian Hospital' is a poem essentially contemplating nature, food, music, life, death, and the culture in which they live.

'Casting Our Nets Into Unremitting Drifts' is a panoramic nature poem juxtaposing the growth of a child with the seasonal nature of her surroundings.

'Road Trip Sestina' uses the Sestina form to illustrate the small repetitions of care within the macro of this trip, maybe a cancer sufferer's final road trip.

'Finally Offered His Dream Audition for the NY Philharmonic, my father turned it down' is a poem essentially about the fear of success and how crippling it could be to a whole life but also to the lives of their children.

Many of the highly commended poems experiment with form or language or both, and the measure between being on the commended list or a winner was at times less than a hair's width.

Now, let me introduce you to the winning poems.

3rd placed poem, 'Why I Kissed The Dead Man' is an exercise in radical empathy and how proximity can build love incrementally. It also accentuates the idea that you don't have to be blood-related to love as if you're blood-related. It also highlights that in death, who knows what seems like a natural reaction or thing to do.

2nd placed poem, 'Prayer w/o Punctuation,' uses the form of a prayer but resonates more like a meditation. The questions in the poem act as a form of thinking, an exercise in not knowing while being achingly aware of both dreamlike and dystopic contextual surroundings. The effect is cinematic in its move from thought to surroundings. A visionary take on nature.

1st place winner, 'Patient And Daughter Appear Closely Bonded,' pulls us in with a startling narrative hook and proceeds to peel off layer after layer of explanation through associative plot and lands perfectly on symbolism. Striking, surprising, and technically excellent, the poem resonates way beyond its ending.

Again, I want to congratulate all the winners and highly commended poets, and I look forward to seeing what these writers do in the future.

COLIN BARRETT

Short Story Report

Reading the shortlist for this year's Bridport Prize, I began thinking again about the peculiar intensity inherent to the short story. The intensity I am talking about is not one of subject matter, the "what" the story is about. It is an intensity of form.

If longform narratives, most germanely the novel, are capable of achieving their own kinds of intensity, they generally do so by accumulation, by the compounding of event upon event and/or by successive expansive plunges into a character's memory or psychological interior. But novels have time on their side, and given that most novels are, in the most basic sense, a story that happens in time, in their approach to character and plotting they are fundamentally incremental, additive (if not always strictly linear or sequential); in a novel we can watch characters change, bit by bit. They can start out as one type of person, and by the end, be someone different. Plot in novels usually happen in bits too, events unfolding over and within any temporal scale the novelist wishes: hours, weeks, years, decades. We can see the shape of a life and/or incident as it evolves, peaks and subsides in time.

The short story is different. Time is not on the short story writer's side. Consequently, time is a much more condensed, pressurized element, both in the story and how it acts on the story. This is a pressure on form and influences everything from the depiction of character, to how that character exists in the world of the short story, to how that world exists in time.

By definition, change in a short story cannot be depicted novelistically, as a graduated series of events or instances unfolding across a given expanse of time. A short story can of course depict a moment of change, but it cannot depict the leadup to that change (or not very much of it, at any rate) – only the final precipitating spark. So change (of circumstances, of self) when it arrives in a short story, often arrives as a kind of shattering or undoing, an abrupt realignment, the breakage or disruption of some established pattern.

This shattering or disruption may take subtle forms; it might not at all be some dramatic outburst or climactic confrontation, it might in fact be barely discernible on the surface of the story (and to the characters themselves, sometimes discernible not at all). It may manifest merely as a

11

moment of arrest or a gesture of negation, an act of withdrawal or episode of incapacitation. But it does happen, and no matter how it happens, what it usually means is that a veil is parted and a character (or again, perhaps only the reader) sees through the illusion of the self, the very world, the story has created.

The short story is a violent form in this sense. Destabilizing. The world in the short story is not voluminous or continuous or durable. It is intimate and contingent and metamorphic. Character, too, is provisional and frangible. This is why the short story's prevailing mode tends to the revelatory, the epiphanic. As the narrator puts it at the end of Frank O'Connor's story 'The Guests Of the Nation': "And anything that ever happened to me after I never felt the same about again."

This is something like what I mean when I think about the peculiar intensity of the short story.

The best stories on this year's shortlist achieved these intensities, by pleasurably and thought provokingly exploiting the peculiar pressures of the form of the short story.

STARLINGS – Tripti is the proud, difficult, ruthlessly guarded mother of Richa, one of several young victims of a predatory gang and still naively in love with the man who groomed her. When a reporter shows up looking to tell Richa's side of the story, Tripti is faced with a difficult choice. The material in this story is highly charged and emotive, but the author handles it with skill and control by grounding the narrative in the perspective of the wonderfully memorable Tripti, whose hard edges and unapologetic, incandescent rage are depicted with moving compassion and lucidity.

VISITORS – Teenager 'Ken' McKensie is left keeping the lights on in the Canadian auto business her profligate, drug addled older brother inherited after the death of their father. This story has energy, ambition and bite, always moving out and beyond the expected.

DIGESTIBLE – Ingrid works with Mr Guratsky in his prop design and puppetry workshop. When her latest assignment has her building an enormous foam intestine for a play its participants insist is "not a horror", she falls into the sights of a charismatic actor, Mark. Strange, offbeat and unexpectedly poignant.

THE INVENTED LANGUAGES OF ADELA ARKANI – A grandfather works as a labourer alongside his disaffected son Xavi and his adored granddaughter, Adela, for a company that requires all its' adult employees to take an experimental drug that incapacitates their ability to speak in daylight, thus theoretically making them more productive, efficient workers. Reminiscent of the eerie, tech-dystopian allegories of George Saunders, this story wears its conceit lightly, unfolding with poetic grace.

ONE GOOD THING – Mrs Silifa, an accomplished and capable academic, a contented widower in her sixties, discovers she might be pregnant by her much younger boyfriend Ben. Then Ben's cousin comes to visit. A funny, sharp, poised and poignant story.

IN CANADA, WE TRAIN OUR DOGS TO SMELL FIRE – In deepest rural Canada, a teenage girl and her dog join a band of rough-hewn local men and boys as they desperately attempt to fight a vast forest fire – "the sprawl" – by setting a series of precise controlled burns. A thrilling, muscular story, full of physical dynamism and laced with deft character moments.

STEEL GLASS – Jayanthi, helped by the impoverished local laundry lady Bayanti, illegally cremate the body of Jayanthi's violent, alcoholic husband in a public park during the height of the pandemic. A story of unflinching intensity and lingering power.

MOTHER VERSUS DEEP BLUE – The narrator recalls the time he and his mother, an artist famous for her abstract representations of the matches of famous chess players – travel to watch Gary Kasparov's famous defeat by the supercomputer Deep Blue. Understated, tight, and playful.

MARGOT – An actress has an idle affair with the series script writer of the show in which she plays her most famous role, the titular Margot, as they negotiate a European press junket. Spare, uneasily hazy and haunting.

THE CHILD IS A MOTHER TOO – A Chinese American illustrator living in New York negotiates an unexpected pregnancy while mourning the recent death of her mother in China. This story takes an ostensibly familiar premise to strange, bracing, and at times visionary places.

In THIRD place CINCINNATI. Ryan is a washed out former junior tennis player, now languishing in the suburbs with his elderly father and taking care of his nine year old niece, Thump, after his brother, Thump's father, disappeared on a bender. Thump persuades Ryan to enter a tennis tournament in Cincinnati as a wild card.

'Cincinnati' is a warm and funny story, shaded with fine characterisation and punctuated by several outwardly low key reversals and twists that nonetheless surprise and move the reader.

In second place is THE BOY. Teenager Eddie, off school and drunk after a lazy day in the park, and stuck in the middle of an increasingly fractious texting back and forth with his girlfriend, encounters a stray dog and accompanies it to the house of a man named Konwani, whom he assumes is the dog's owner. Konwani admits he is not, but invites Eddie in for a drink.

Written in the close third, 'The Boy' is a sophisticated portrait of Eddie, who is simultaneously handsome, and charming, easy-going to the point of complacency, innocent and eager for experience, and seemingly unaware of his innate capability for incidental cruelty. The events that shock his world and jar his sense of self are relatively small but expertly depicted in this sharp, assured story.

In first place, AN INTERVENTION. Nafhat wakes up one day to discover that her hapless, depressive, alcoholic father has disappeared, a fact met with calm, unnerving dismissiveness by Nafhat's beautiful, green eyed mother and older brothers. Despite her protestations, the rest of her family insist he will no doubt return, sooner or later. A story of beautiful control, attentiveness and discipline, at once dreamlike and grittily realistic, 'An Intervention' is a story of absences and circling malice, a memorable and lingering ghost story.

CHRISTOPHER ALLEN

Flash Fiction Report

Thank you to the editors and organisers of The Bridport Prize for asking me to judge the flash fiction portion of the 2023 competition. Congratulations on your 50th anniversary. Reading for the prize has been a great pleasure and honour.

What makes a compelling micro? This is so difficult. Each of the stories I read does something moving with the space, so narrowing the field took weeks. The top eight narratives are all memorable and innovative in their various ways.

All the highly commended micros are singular examples of what's possible within the word-count constraint of the micro. 'God Save the King' shows how affecting a subtle list story can be. 'The Sandcastle' defamiliarizes the all-too-familiar deterioration that comes with age and dementia. The analogy in 'Anna Wonders Whether Birds Will Build a Nest with Cat Hair' is memorable and relevant, as is the central image in 'Patterns'. And finally, among the highly commended, I loved the apocalyptic frenzy of 'On the Nextdoor App'.

Setting plays an important role in all three of the top narratives. From winter in Indiana to a town hit by a killer tornado to the geography of a simple sofa, I'm excited by the possibilities of place in all three of these moments of being. Oddly—or perhaps just a sign of the times—a jolt of devastation also plays a leading role in these stories. Devastating situations alone, though, can't guarantee great writing. Sadly, if we live long enough, we'll all experience our share of devastation. Kudos to writers who manage to convey these stories in a layered, innovative and affecting way.

In 'Carve' the narrator asserts ownership of her life—with a butcher knife. The setting is winter in Indiana but more the phantom feeling of a perpetrator's grip. The subject of domestic abuse is perennial in flash, and it's important that editors don't become desensitized—which is a challenge since we see so many stories of abuse. The same is true for loss.

Tonally, 'The Sofa' has the weighty atmosphere of a French drama, each detail pregnant with loss. It's a devastating situation: a mother and daughter hamstrung by the death of the husband/father, a person full of optimism for a future in a new country. The sofa, the last purchase before the father's death, works so well as a symbol of their lost hope and security. In the end, we are left with the question 'What now?' inviting us to imagine the paralyzing horror of starting over again.

By chance, the first-place entry, 'The Whirling Aftermath', also ends with a question: 'Would you blame me?' The interrogative is an effective device to encourage and more importantly *expand* the readers' investment in the possible future outcomes of the story. The narrative is a classic breathless paragraph, echoing the mayhem of the story's weather and the energy of the narrator's sexual desire. This form has become a classic workshop task, so flash editors read quite a lot of these pieces with equal amounts of hope and scepticism. The syntax of a good one-sentence story feels organic and necessary, as it does in 'The Whirling Aftermath'. Literal environmental devastation is the setting, but the writer chooses to have their tornado strew sweets all over the town. What a bountifully messy image and what a welcome subversion of the very idea of devastation.

Congratulations to everyone.

AMANDA QUAID

Patient and Daughter Appear Closely Bonded

My toddler takes a bite of tater tot and tells me
    she wants me to die.

The social worker says I should *respond* and not
    react to things like that

so I ask *why* she says she wants me to die
    as though it's just

a thought-provoking notion that has never
    crossed my mind.

She thinks for a moment, chewing, her tiny lips
    stained with blueberry juice.

"I want you to die so you can show me
    how to die."

I take that phrase and tuck it in my breast—she's
    given me a gift, I know

a task or blessing or could it be—would you not
    call it *permission*—

"And you could come back as a peacock!" she cries
    with a grin

"And so could I, and then we could be friends!"
    She cackles at me and I smile

back at her and see us in the next
   go-round, two peacocks

preening our plumes in the Sri Lankan sun,
   finally peers and bickering

over the last mangosteen
   in the grove.

ALYSON KISSNER

Prayer w/o Punctuation

I want to be holy somewhere else

where wild horses articulate
the expanse of a wheatfield where sweetgrass + wolf moss break
the gathering pines

trees
jagged

w/ conditions of salt dear god

the sky here has gone home lilac + disordered
w/ airplanes

where is the rain

b/c memory is an inadequate speaker where the moon is concerned
I am hushdrunk

will you tell me

did the nightjar vanish in the temperate dark did I
miss the signal for snow

the forest fires of the pacific northwest are all we have left of the cold but I
am still here I want

an ocean as wide as blue flowers columbines branching like silver grazing
like caribou possibly our own shadows will collect themselves like rivers
in another life the past its own revision in symmetry
swimming sidebyside pls

just give me an honest storm a sudden thunder a reset clean water my mother
perched above my childhood like a peregrine
protecting her young

god

if I am ageing I want to hold her god
against my tongue + whisper him backwards

I want to summon what can never be touched

LANCE LARSEN

Why I Kissed the Dead Man

Because he took a final breath but the sky
        went on and on, because the nurse turned off
            the beeping machines, because he
was my father-in-law, because I love
        his daughter Jacqui and she kissed him first
            and I wanted to kiss whatever she kissed,

because the skin on his neck and face
        were still warm, because I loved him
            from afar the way one loves oily reliable tools
and stories about designing Cold War
        sonar smarter than God, because love
            has sink holes in it lost rivers disappearing

into the Delphic earth then returning
        freshened 10,000 years later, because he spent
            his last weeks shredding things junk mail
canceled checks yellowed engineering books
        page by page, little metallic teeth digesting
            his life, because he had seven full trash bags

squirreled away in his bedroom and hoped
        to walk them to the curb himself,
            because wouldn't it be lovely to toss
that confetti off the hospital roof and let
        a ferocious wind dust the city with pieces
            of him, because I hoped to save Jacqui

from something dark and intractable
       and human and sour but couldn't,
              because there were unmapped continents
in her kiss and a hidden waterfall,
       because there was only electrician's tape
              in mine and wire snips and once

an impromptu trip to buy a smoke detector,
       because fathers are so damned hard to love
              in this life and fathers-in-law harder,
because I wanted and still want someone
       to kiss me after I die, someone with three
              days' growth of beard who doesn't have to.

MARA BERGMAN

Fear
After Dorianne Laux

It was fear from the start – of sinking in quicksand
though Jones Beach was devoid of quicksand.
Fear of alligators and crocodiles; fear of sharks.
Fear of the teenager I crashed my bicycle into
on the pavement, fearing she was the new babysitter.
Fear of sleep when it was still light, my parents outside
gardening, and fear of being alone at night, the darkness
under my bed, in my closet, the darkness on the stairs. Fear
of horses, horseshoe crabs, jellyfish. Of hurricanes, tidal waves,
volcanoes. Fear of nuclear war, crouching against the corridor wall
at school and fear of outer space and loss of gravity, loss
of breath. Of vastness and distance. Fear of one knee dislocating, then
the other, and of falling while crossing a road. Of being crushed
in Central Park after a concert, my friends holding hands and running,
then fear of missing the bus to Penn Station, missing the train
and never getting home. Fear of driving. Fear of not knowing
how to kiss or when to let the kissing go further, and how far.
Of being trapped: the cave with a space so small we had to
take off our helmets to squeeze through. Fear of never getting out.
Of winter and the quiet. Of snow, and cold. Of mountains
covered in snow, the cow-path down to the town from my dorm
screeching with music, long-haired boys smoking joints; of classes
and the fear of not being good enough, or worthy, of not being
in the right place at the right time. Fear of arriving late,
missing a plane, of forgetting my passport. Fear
of jumping in water, doing a backflip, staying submerged.
Of swimming pools: the one at Lori's house, the Olympic pool
at Nassau Beach, the one at camp that at night
froze under the stars. And the lake, so cold – fear of swimming
out to a raft not knowing what lurked below and the fear of being left there
surrounded only by mountains. Of freezing. Of fish nibbling toes. Eels,
something bigger. Of being alone. Swimming as darkness fell,
light fading and not being able to see, then not seeing anything,

the fear of going blind. The cold and wet. Feeling lost. Fear of the last day
of summer as one by one the cabanas shut, the snack bar, the metal chair
piled with rescued bathing caps and goggles. Forgotten towels.
Everything closing down, packing up. Finishing. I feared the finishing.
The goodbyes. Any ending. The quiet that followed.

KIZZIAH BURTON

Casting Our Nets In The Unremitting Drifts

Miles deep into the Bosque del Apache, my daughter and I
study the patterns of a sedge of sandhill cranes teaching their young

to sleep standing up in water, between the sandbars, in the wide-
open, braided channels. Like me, they worry about wolves.

The blue herons fly in at sunset to sleep in the trees.
Another sound, flying low, is resounding in the wetlands.

Sometimes I hear it. The sound reminds me of the monk's *aum*.
More like the earth's *hum* tunneling through the night.

                              *   *   *

In winter, we light piñon fires for the spirits of the shores. Flames
in the dark to show the way. Under a wolf moon, we walk the river's edge

in the wet caliche, a slurry of snow and clay soaked into the shallows.
The fires behind us, burning down, fading. My daughter wades deeper

into the scrolling sands to read the river. No tide – more of a swaying
cold, swaying night. She feeds her vows to the slipperings –

yellow speckled and green-striped basses (while I try to estimate the risk
of standing too close to the edge, gazing into someone else's abyss).

                              *   *   *

In late spring, we shake the trees for apples. When our baskets
are full we walk home through the moon-barked cottonwoods

glowing along the river. The sad downcast whistle
of a finch reaches us. (I measure the effect on my little girl

25

going on, after toiling the realm for her sister, still lost
in a wild landscape.) I pick up and carry my worn-out child,

under a sky quiet as the cotton-like seed casings floating
weightless in the air. It looks like it is snowing in the desert.

*   *   *

No one made us walk the high desert oasis where it meets
the river down by the old town. No one made us sing out

her name. No one made the wind swallow our calls and rattles.
You want to know what made us wade, night after night,

into the desert, cast our nets in the unremitting drifts.
A girl can drown in a desert like this.

MARY MULHOLLAND

Grandma's Book of Receipts

When she kept emigrating she held on
to her recipes, which she called her *cooking
receipts*, but received only

raised eyebrows after settling in England
if she made pepperpot or garlic pork.
She'd left her family behind in Guyana

to find a new life. When they joined her,
they found her scrubbing the dust
till no trace remained of what they knew

or had been through. She fed them
caldo verde, after discarding the unwanted
outer leaves, wrapped a secret in each

she cooked. Once she dreamt of green
cabbage and woke knowing her husband
had been betrayed by a friend; he knew it too.

And o how the smell of dying persisted
after pegging out *bacalhau* to dry,
eye sockets and brains pecked clean by gulls,

fish flapping like underwear, like ghosts
of large bats. And she sang the *fado* to give voice
to souls born of sadness and the sea.

She had three hundred and sixty-five dishes
for this, was raised to believe a wife must eat
a pastry a day and never remove her ring.

She'd win that pie-flinging prize with her *pasteis
de nata.* Her husband's name meant prize: Premio.
It was all he left. After starching her daily habits

in private she sipped *vinho verde.* He was too young
to go, too greenly trusting. Sometimes she'd blur
with the sweetness of her roots, her lips spelling

malasadas, rum cake, *queijo de serra,*
then she'd turn the page: no place for sentiment.
Life was no holy picture of ewes on a star mountain.

Taking a sharp knife, she'd peel back the skin,
cut it raw, then sieve grit from good grain.
Occasionally her pressure cooker would explode.

JEAN O'BRIEN

The Sadness is On Me / Tá Brón Orm

My daughter's abandoned rite of passage,
her teenage guitar, is propped against
my bookshelves. Neither of us know
how to play it. Casually I pull my
finger-tips across still taut strings.
Its vibrations cause a melancholy sound,
like breath drawn across vocal cords
or the sough of wind moaning
in marram grass.
I name the feeling — *Tá brón orm*

(*The sadness is on me*)
These are ghost words to me.
I phrase and rephrase my English,
that language that writer Con Holahan said
was *woven on a Gaelic loom.*
We cannot give full voice to
the open wound, the constantly
picked skin on our vowels,
as if we are forever spinning
the cursing stones counter clockwise,
against the sun. *Tá brón orm*

I don't remember that our tongues
stretched like the animal skins
spread taut over the wicker frame
of the currach, that rides the swell
with everyone facing backwards
with oars for words and rowing
furiously. I read somewhere
that there was no word in Irish back then
for a female poet, so we write our own
Áers or Mallacht poems and leave
the very air we breath sparked blue.

29

The sadness is on me for a language
elusive, yet still flickers, a small votive
flame that gutters in the dark,
and smells of bog smoke,
producing infinitesimal calculus.
The tattered line of breath catches
somewhere in my synapsis.
a gutteral ghost. *Grá mo chroí.*

ERIN O'LUANAIGH

Road Trip Sestina

Across and down, we take the country's measure
like a seamstress fitting a woman for a dress.
Beside me, my mother, a pillow on her chest,
maps out each road and highway, stitch by stitch.
Neither of us has driven through the West, crossed
the mountains rippling the continent's wide veil,

seen the Badlands, the Tetons, the waterfalled vales
out of Bierstadt. At night in our hotel, we measure
two kinds of progress: she, marking guidebooks, crossing
off names; I, surveying the skin beneath her dressing,
changing bandages, checking every pale stitch
that snakes from her sides to the middle of her chest,

strewing stained coffee tables and plywood chests
with wrappers. The cancer looked like a veil,
the doctors said, a sheet of lacework stitched
through the tissue. (They took "extreme measures.")
I lay out her clothes for tomorrow, then help her dress
for bed, putting aside her scapular and cross.

When she returns home, flies back alone across
the country (TSA wands beeping over her chest),
she'll have to face her new body, take her dresses
to a friend, a seamstress, to see if she might veil
the loss with fabric, or else take measurements
for custom clothes. She'll cry at not having a stitch

to wear... But for now, she indulges my itch
for travel, wants to think only of the next cross-
road, of the nearest park entrance, of measuring
me against the world's-largest-something, of The Hope Chest,
where she hopes to find "cowboy gear" (to no avail)
and I model a 70's sheath just like a dress

she once wore. Soon, we'll punch in the address
of our last stop, drive a highway that stitches
over the ribs of the Wasatch, its peaks veiled
in smoke that falls to the valley floor, and cross
into Salt Lake—my street the lowest drawer in the chest
of the hillside. My mother tries to reassure me,

tugging at her cross, that she feels better. Her chest
hardly hurts anymore. Her stitches freshly dressed,
she says goodbye in a voice measured but veiled.

JENNY PAGDIN

Ursa Major

I wanted a deckchair on our roof for stargazing and though we don't have a garden the roof is flat and I remember rotating fluorescent star-charts above my head, aged ten, but they were mapped for the wrong hemisphere so I never learnt the constellations until over bacon sandwiches an ex-boyfriend showed me the Plough in his parents' garden and on the evening I put all the knives in the toaster, and they sectioned me, I felt like I was in handcuffs and I prefer doors now because then I was always going for the window, pulling on the plastic handle like I couldn't work it and roaring my lion's roar and the police were in our bedroom, the neighbours at the door with deckchairs, and Noah's little voice below and Orion's belt re-forming in the Velux, and the policewoman saying he was fine he was having his tea and between my coarse screams a rubber black bar over me in the ambulance like the Big Dipper and the paramedics' insinuations and the hospital guards weeing on the floor of A&E and pushing my head back into a seizure and planning to rape me, the one with the spangled arms and the one who was super tall in that room which moved like a lift and sometimes now I feel the full moon zing like a ten-pee piece on my tongue, and I wheel my bike through, and shrug, running through my constellations like a tarot, my finger grazing on each star, trying to make them fit.

MARGARET RAY

Noodles, August, the Courtyard of New York-Presbyterian Hospital
For D, for E, and for Simon

My love has gone North to the ocean to scatter some of his mother's ashes
so she can float on the wind of the world she loved, but I am elsewhere,

I am in lower Manhattan because my sister has just had a baby–
here I am, feeling tender toward every fragile-looking creature I see.

My mother and I take turns going up to visit within the hospital's limits,
and we sit in the courtyard of New York-Presbyterian sharing noodles

before we can gaze at him again for another hour each. My sister
has just had a baby and there are common sparrows

all around the cement courtyard, and some of them approach
my mother and me, utterly unafraid, while we eat our noodles, here they are

making earnest eye contact: an ask, they know we have food,
we are doing the behavior of humans who have food we might offer

or drop. Tiny black dinosaur-eyes looking up. Beads
of darkest ocean water. I've been paying attention more lately,

watching sparrows near my apartment, and that is how I recognize
the fluttering-wing gesture fledglings do to ask a parent

for seeds. Delicate thing, a gesture so instinctual and guileless,
aimed here at me. I am suddenly stunned by these slight,

ordinary birds thriving here, I may never
have a baby of my own, the noodles are delicious and fresh

and spicy, my love is in another state, a summer study-abroad group
cuts through the courtyard in their matching blue backpacks,

bubbles of their teenage Italian rise into the vibrating summer evening,
I must move so deliberately, gently,

gently, and scatter only what can be put to use.

JOYCE SCHMID

Finally offered his dream audition for the NY Philharmonic, my father turned it down

When he woke,
he found the bird cage open

and a golden streak of light
from cage to window—

his canary
moving through the after-image
of its melody,

diffusing through the glass
to claim the sky.

My father hopped
into the cage
and closed the door behind him.

All he sang forever after
was that song.

JOELLE SCHUMACHER

blasphemy, americana

somebody tell miles davis / the reagans are out, trump is in;
i wanna see jazz / knock the devil out the white house /
i wanna see blues / sweep mississippi off its feet /
i want wojnarowicz clawing clambersome out his grave,
& eating politicians / alive, i want people / in the streets, &
ribbons / in the streetlights, &biscuits
rising in the kitchen / i want yr thumb in my mouth
like a reason / to believe in god / like scientific proof / like
proof / in paradox

i wanna see / you / inside me, the way mary / got god / inside her /
i wanna bear fruit, i want
the rain to rapture / me whole

i want healthcare & block parties & a whole hillside of believin i want
the green to climb like a man on his bootstraps
out of whatever holy ashland the revolution leaves us with
i want a hillside full of scripture /
lone church prayers ringing proud echo in the desert /
i want the mountaintops down here
and down here

to be up there / i want water in flint and power in a blackout /
i want you /in the car
choking
like i am not holy /
and me /in the car
choking
because i am holy

and as it's all burning / i want to ask the fire
what is holier than this –
the ability to die? / america is dying /
but you still play the blues inside me / and still / the road / is driving

tell me something about a homeland
and i will tell you something about blood
something about minneapolis
and a whole cafeteria red with AK47'ed kids /
bonewhite cross & bloodred lynching /

oh sweet toothed liberty / oh green burial ground /
oh fields of rotting fruits /
oh bloodstained church bench /
oh plastic bleeding landfill /
and the girl saying oh god – oh god – oh god /
as she rocks / in her daddy's backseat

WILLIAM WYLD

What we think about Tintoretto

We both know what we think about Tintoretto,
me and my father, we both know why he placed Christ
at the centre, his benign face and bright halo
the source of all the light; we know he drew it twice
before he got it right. We both know what we think
about abstraction, why early Mondrian is so
close toned, and how those dark and simple landscapes link
to the sparse grids of his maturity. We know
the right proportions for a picture frame, why my
mother left, and just how high a painting should be
hung. We know Titian's sky is lapis lazuli,
that material and meaning overlap. He
knows a lot my father, we talk for hours, we plan.
I do a very good impression of a man.

TOM MILES

An Intervention

Everything fails, with a disaffected sigh, and the apartment slides into near darkness. Nafhat drops her pen and looks towards the ceiling, where the shape of the living room window is faintly projected by a streetlight. It is a small flat with very few moving parts and the most static object, generally speaking, is her father: a rotund, grumbling, somnolent presence at this time of any evening, once the turf accountants have closed and a quarter bottle of brandy – the cost price of which he has been prudent enough to withhold from his foiled investments – has been unhurriedly consumed. He is already asleep. Nafhat decides not to wake him.

She rises from her desk, takes two steps across the room and reaches over the arm of the battered armchair in which her father sits, snoring, and retrieves a cigarette lighter from his trouser pocket. She proceeds into the hallway, which is very dark, and finds the electricity meter on the wall, guided by the flame from the lighter. She takes the key from the meter and places a finger over the empty slot. Nafhat allows the flame to die and for the lighter to cool. She waits for thirty seconds, moves her finger, then places the lighter as close as she can to the vacant aperture in the meter before striking the flint with a flick of her thumb. The meter clicks and the flat moans into life. A note of momentary agitation is audible from the living room but by the time Nafhat returns to her desk her father is snoring again.

She has finished her homework and is about to brush her teeth when the doorbell rings. It is too early for either her brothers or her mother to be returning home and her heart shivers momentarily. She stands behind the front door, sensing that chaos, only chaos, can lay beyond it.

"Is that Nafi Yes?" A man's voice, not unkind, using her nickname. "We need to speak to Baba Nizam most urgently. May we enter?"

She opens the door, just an inch. A smell of warm leather and cologne. Two very large men stand in the corridor, both are dressed in black and are wearing heavy jewellery. The man closest to her winks and offers her a sweet. She takes it, instinctively, and pops it under her tongue.

No-one can quite comprehend how Omar Nizam found such a beauty of a wife. She is tall, green-eyed and very fair. She plays the flute with both flair and precision. In fact she is a little older than her husband, though one could not guess such a thing. Time rests easily on her. She is preparing breakfast when her daughter enters the small kitchen.

"Good morning Mama."

"Good morning Nafi, did you sleep well?"

"Very well, thank you," says the little girl. "Where is Baba?"

"I think he must have left very early," her mother says. "He was in his chair when I returned home, snoring away. When I woke he was gone." Nafhat frowns. There is an unpleasant taste in her mouth and she cannot remember if she brushed her teeth before falling asleep. The smell of cooking in the kitchen disguises the faintest trace of cedarwood which might otherwise be detectable on her nightdress.

"It's not like him," she says. "He always wishes me a good day at school."

"He's a very busy man," her mother remarks, laughing to herself.

As Nafhat stands before the hallway mirror, knotting her tie and adjusting her scarf, Jahan, the older of her brothers, appears from their room. She sticks a leg out to prohibit his passage to the bathroom. He hops from foot to foot with two hands shielding his groin.

"Let me get to the loo, Nafi Yes."

"Was Baba at home when you got back last night?"

"Of course," Jahan says. "Snoring like a Kawasaki. Foot down, Nafi Yes, before I pee myself."

Jahan and her younger brother Parvez have the good fortune, denied to Nafhat, of bearing their mother's looks. They wear their beards very neat and short and their hair long and both have numerous girlfriends that Mama is not allowed to know about. Jahan is studying accountancy and Parvez is interested in computers but for the moment they work in a restaurant halfway up the Lane which accommodates braying city folk at lunchtime and nervous tourists in the evening. They seem to love and despise their jobs with alternating and equal vehemence. Satisfied with the neatness of her dress, though disappointed, as ever, with the plain, round face which looks back at her from the frameless mirror, Nafhat returns to the kitchen to kiss her mother goodbye. Jahan emerges from the bathroom in time to squeeze her shoulders and she pulls the front door closed, feeling her father's absence like the half-shaded memory of an important task, doomed to remain forever undone.

An Intervention

Omar Nizam is not there when his daughter returns from school. Nafhat tries to stay awake to confront the rest of the family with the fact of his absence, but falls asleep instead.

Nafhat sits in her father's chair, which exhales betting shop odours when she shifts her weight. She watches as her mother moves around the kitchen, preparing breakfast once again, as if nothing has changed. A thick knot of hair, still remarkably black, balances on Mrs Nizam's head as she reaches into cupboards and cracks eggs into a saucepan. A long neck, which seems longer still when her hair is up; large, clever peridot eyes which she turns on her only daughter.

"Have you eaten, Nafi?"

Nafhat redirects her gaze to a zig-zag of screw holes on the doorframe, evidence that there must once have been a door which separated the two spaces. She closes her eyes (small, the colour of wet mud, not unintelligent) and tries to remember when the door was removed.

"File not found," she whispers.

"Nafi?" A note of tightness has entered her mother's voice. The girl nods. "He will come back, you know," Mrs Nizam says. "He won't have gone far." Nafhat's head throbs with the threat of weeping but she swallows the sensation somehow, then clears her throat.

"I've got to get to school, Mama," she says.

The school is a squabble of single storey buildings constructed during a period of grave social inequality and limited faith in the capacity of primary education to right any wrongs. The squat collection of prefabs and shanty town lean-tos are a kind of distant rebuke to medieval church architecture. It takes Nafhat twenty minutes of desultory ambling to get there from Boundary Gardens. Like most inner city schools it is under-staffed, but the majority of teachers are young and as yet unjaded. Miss Perkins, Nafhat's teacher, is the same age as Jahan. She crouches slightly to welcome each of her pupils into the classroom. Dust (bookdust, child-dust) sweats on the caged radiators and a smell like old chocolate fills the room.

"No smile today, Nafhat?" Miss Perkins asks, and regrets doing so immediately, as the face of the small brown girl filing past her spasms into a mask of distress and hot, deferred tears. "Go and sit over there," Miss Perkins says, gesturing to a chair at the back of the classroom. "I'll be with you in one moment." Nafhat takes the tissue which her teacher has conjured from thin air, apparently, and sits, feeling relieved and humiliated all at once.

41

"My father has disappeared and my family don't care," Nafhat says. She is calm now. They are in a room she has never been in before, an office of some sort, half-filled with exercise books and with geraniums dying on the window sill. Miss Perkins absorbs this information.

"When you say 'disappeared', what do you mean, Nafhat?"

"He hasn't been at home for two days. Some men came to see him on Tuesday, at bedtime, and I haven't seen him since. Mama and my brothers pretended he was there yesterday but he wasn't. This morning Mama told me not to worry, that he would come back. So he is gone, definitely, and I'm the only person who is bothered about it." The teacher nods.

"Has he gone away before?"

"No, never."

"When you were little, perhaps? Would you remember that?" Nafhat thinks. She does not remember a time when her father was not falling asleep in his chair in the evening. But once there must have been a door between the kitchen and the living room.

"Perhaps," she says.

"Okay," says Miss Perkins. "I'm going to speak to your Mummy and we'll see what we can sort out. You wait here."

"No," Nafhat says. "Mama will be upset with me." Miss Perkins makes a face which Nafhat cannot read, then reaches across the table and takes her by the wrist.

"No-one is going to be upset with you, Nafhat, I promise. And no-one is going to hurt you."

There is a police car parked on the corner of Camlet Street when Nafhat returns home. "They've found him and brought him home!" she thinks, climbing the first flight of stairs two at a time, then slowing, as she admits the possibility of other outcomes. The door to the flat is open, dark clothing and humourless conversation perceptible within. As Nafhat hurries into the hallway she listens for her father's voice, a distinctive voice thickened by tens of thousands of cigarettes, but retaining always a note of childish wheedling. She cannot hear it. She hangs up her schoolbag and steps into the living room in which the stooped, oblate figure of Omar Nizam is nowhere to be seen. The police are there, a man and a woman. The woman is holding a notebook and a pen both of which appear to be too small for her to comfortably use. Mrs Nizam stands in the bright rectangle between the kitchen and the living room, where there was undoubtedly once a door. She has her coat on and is clutching a counterfeit Gucci handbag under one arm. She looks at her daughter and the policewoman follows her gaze, turning to smile at Nafhat. The policewoman's coat makes an unpleasant sound as she moves.

"This is Nafhat," says Mrs Nizam. "Her supper is in the fridge. And I have to get to work." She walks towards her youngest child, allowing her eyes to widen momentarily before passing into the hall. Then her heels click away down the concrete stairs.

"Your mother said that she doesn't know exactly where your father is, however she's sure he'll come back very soon." Nafhat stirs the food in the saucepan and nods slowly. "Sometimes," the policewoman continues, "people go away, not because anything bad has happened to them…"

"We think your Dad is okay," the policeman says, interrupting. "Nothing to worry about."

"Are you going to look for him?" Nafhat asks, turning towards the policeman with a wooden spoon raised at an accusatory angle. There is a pause.

"Do you have a picture of him," he asks, "a recent photo?" Nafhat pushes the saucepan to the back of the stove and weaves past the constables into the living room. She takes a small silver frame from the top of the TV set and hands it to the policeman.

"His beard is longer now," she says. The policeman studies the photograph while Nafhat looks at his name badge. CONSTABLE MCCULLOUGH. She wonders how the name might be pronounced. It seems to have too many letters put together in no sensible order. The policeman passes the photograph to his colleague, who nods and sticks her bottom lip out as she looks at Omar Nizam.

"We'll keep an eye out for him," the policewoman says, as she crosses the living room and replaces the picture frame on the television.

Mrs Nizam is a manager at a factory which makes pre-packed sandwiches for petrol stations and convenience stores. It is her cousin's company and Mrs Nizam has a small share in the business, a fact which she conceals from everyone, her family included, because of a certain personal delicacy, and because the cousin in question is involved in other enterprises which are less savoury than mass-produced Coronation Chicken. She works the evening shift and returns home at two in the morning. On this particular morning, a Friday, Mrs Nizam finds a note on her pillow from Nafhat, explaining that she had not contacted the police, and had only told her teacher about Baba because she had cried in class and didn't want to tell lies. Mrs Nizam folds the note and puts it in the drawer of her bedside table. She walks to the living room and crouches beside her daughter who is asleep on the sofa. She kisses Nafhat's hair and one small round eye opens. Mrs Nizam reaches under the blanket which covers her daughter and finds a hand, which she squeezes lightly.

"Come," she says. "Sleep in with Mama tonight." Nafhat rises as if spellbound and follows her mother without saying a word.

For a week, and then another, Nafhat goes along with pretence that nothing has changed. She stirs in her sleep most nights, registering the sour smell of sweat on silk, as her mother lies down beside her. Her brothers continue to tease her, but make no reference to their father, or to the devotion shown by Nafi Yes to her useless, idle Baba. At school the other children are preoccupied with football or dance routines and Miss Perkins knows better than to enquire after the missing parent. No-one needs to deal with a little girl's tears, be they tears of relief or ongoing anguish, more often than is absolutely necessary.

The pretence, inexorably, becomes a kind of fact. Within a month Omar Nizam ceases to exist, in the most important way: no-one, not even Nafhat, can remember what it was like when he was around. His absence is no longer even a negative value. He is a zero, the figure he has long resembled. His daughter, who is not blind to his faults, but nevertheless holds him in higher esteem than anyone, finds comfort in a new intimacy with her mother and condemns her father to Oblivion.

This new reality persists until one afternoon in mid-October, when on her way home from school, Nafhat is stopped in the street by a lay preacher with a megaphone. He stands in front of her, with a wild surmise and his sweater tucked into his belt. An overflowing waste bin and the city bound traffic on Bethnal Green Road prevent her from passing. The preacher clicks off the megaphone and leans towards her. "You, child, are among the innocents," he hisses. "Suffer little children to come unto me, sayeth the Lord. But thy father and thy mother are not without sin. Unto the Lord they must repent!" Another passer-by removes his shoe and throws it at the preacher and Nafhat hurries away.

Thy father. Omar Nizam. Baba. For the first time in weeks she allows the idea of him to fully occupy her thoughts and realises, with a crescendo of anxiety, that she cannot remember his face. She recalls a beard and thinning hair combed over his scalp, but the rest of his features are a blur. She is heartsick, overwhelmed in a moment, and sobs in the street. Yes, he is not the best man, the best parent that a little girl could wish for, but does he deserve to be forgotten altogether, and so soon? She runs home, takes the photograph from the top of the television and stares at it for a minute or longer, before stuffing it, frame and all, into her schoolbag. Then she sets out to find her father.

"You were late, Nafi, and your coat is soaking wet. I had to hang it over the radiator."

"Sorry, Mama. There was a thing after school."

"I thought I heard you come in," says Mrs Nizam, "but when I came out of the bathroom there was no-one there."

"It wasn't me," says Nafhat. She shivers; for her brothers lying to Mama comes as easily as breathing, but she is fanatically honest, and every mistruth or half-truth diminishes her sense of self. If Nafi Yes stops being a good girl what is left? "Mama?"

"Yes, Nafhat."

"I want to learn the flute. Will you teach me?"

"Of course, my darling."

The streets are slippery with leaves and autumn rain. Nafhat dawdles on her way home from school. She sees Baba Nizam everywhere: emerging from the newsagents with the Racing Post tucked under one arm, peeling the cellophane from a packet of cigarettes, expectorating outside a pub, swearing in a phone box. It is never him, never really him. As half-term approaches she becomes more desperate. She waits for a sympathetic face to emerge from a betting shop here, an off licence there, and pulls the photograph from her schoolbag.

"Do you know this man?" she asks. "Have you seen him?" Some people want to help but cannot. They offer rueful half-smiles and consoling wishes. Others observe that everyone looks like that round here, and her eyes burn with indignation, even as she recognises that there is some degree of truth in this observation. "He looks like my cousin," she is told, often and kindly, which amounts to the same thing.

The afternoons shrink and Nafhat catches a cold. She shelters in doorways, coughing. Even the drunks tell her to go home. The ghosts of her father drift along Bethnal Green Road but when they turn towards the shivering child they wear other faces.

Sometimes the ghosts speak to her.

"What will you say to him, Nafi Yes, if you find him?"

"I'll tell him that I love him and that I want him to come home."

"What if he doesn't want to come back? What if Baba Nizam is happier without you? What will you do then?"

"I will climb on his shoulders and not let go."

It is Omar Nizam who finds Nafhat in the end. She wakes in an unfamiliar space, beneath the covers of a narrow bed. The ceiling is high and the walls are tiled, like a bathroom. Three large windows on one side and a door on the other. A smell of disinfectant. Across the room from her in a narrow bed of his own is a black boy in Spiderman pyjamas. His head is bandaged so that only half of his face, the bottom left half, is visible.

"What happened to you?" Nafhat asks.

"My brother hit me with a chair," the boy says. "It was metal, but it was an accident."

"He must be in a lot of trouble." The boy nods slowly and pouts. Nafhat turns her gaze to the door at the precise moment her father walks through it. He is holding a small bottle containing a yellow liquid.

"Time for your medicine, Nafi Yes," says Omar Nizam.

"Is it really you, Baba?"

"Yes, yes," her father replies. "No time for questions now, just take this and rest." Nafhat studies his face as he pours the liquid into a plastic spoon. He has grown thinner, but is not really thin. His hair is shaved very short where once it swirled sparsely over his head. His beard is neat. His eyes are bright and nervous. "Antibiotics," he says.

"Do you work at the hospital now, Baba?"

"No, Nafi. I'm a businessman, as you know. Just visiting. Had to go on a trip. Rest now, darling girl."

The boy with the bandage tells Nafhat that she has moonomia. She wonders if he has the expertise to make a diagnosis but he explains that he heard the doctor telling her mother.

"Moonomia? Are you sure?"

"That's what he said," the boy affirms. "He showed her a picture. It was black and white. You'll get better though, definitely."

"How is your head?"

"Very itchy. They had to sew my skull back together."

"Goodness."

When Nafhat returns home from the hospital Parvez, unhelpfully perhaps, tells her that if she had not survived they would have put her mortal remains in a room with The Elephant Man.

"Who is The Elephant Man?"

"You know, the deformed guy from the film. They've got his skeleton at the hospital."

"Don't listen to his nonsense, Nafi Yes. Your brother is an idiot."

"Yes, Baba."

"It's true, Baba! You can look it up." Omar Nizam waves away this idea with a regal gesture.

"I have no time for libraries and whatnot," he says. One happy though perhaps unanticipated consequence of his newfound teetotalism is that he now commands the respect of his sons, and the younger boy demurs. His father is respectable. It is still unclear how he makes his money, there is some talk of white goods, but critically he no longer drinks or gambles it away. A new television has appeared in the living room, with a large, shallow screen upon which there is no room for photographs.

Nafhat remains loyal to her previous father, the portly, often breathless man who no-one else could tolerate. The new Omar Nizam is kinder, and listens to her when she complains about school. He smells nicer, or rather he does not smell at all. But she does not really understand, emotionally at least, why the father that she loved despite his faults has been replaced with one who she cannot love despite his qualities. Baba Nizam never needed her, but now he makes no secret of it.

Winter passes and the family settles into new routines. Nafhat still sleeps on the sofa, but is never woken by her father's snoring. Omar Nizam has reoccupied the conjugal bed. On a warm spring Sunday Mrs Nizam walks along Columbia Road, looking for a houseplant to add colour to the bathroom. Her husband and daughter follow in echelon. Two large men in leather jackets approach Mrs Nizam and bow to her, as if she were some Mesopotamian queen. They converse briefly, while Baba Nizam examines a great eruption of gladioli on a nearby stall.

"Who were those men?" Nafhat asks a moment later, when the two parties have reconvened and proceeded in opposite directions.

"Friends of my cousin," her mother answers. "Good men. They help people who have lost their way. Like shepherds."

"They don't look like shepherds. Shepherds have dogs."

"Oh, I think they have dogs, when necessary." Mrs Nizam smiles. "They're going to bring you a flute for you to practice on, Nafi. Isn't that kind?" Nafhat's father, breathless as she fondly remembers him being, places a hand on her shoulder. His hand is shaking.

"Sorry, Mama?"
"Isn't it kind of them to bring you a flute?" her mother says.
"Yes," says Nafhat.

ALEX LUKE

The Boy

Eddie had baby-deer legs, scrawny and endless, and delicate hips from which the glory of his upper body spread like a Japanese fan. He was seventeen, so there was still time for his bottom half to bulk out, but he wasn't sure he wanted this. People joked that he was shaped like a cocktail glass, and the joke had awe behind it. He was just a centimetre too strange-looking to be written off as another light-skinned, square-headed ASOS model. He tossed his black ringlets out of his eyes and let them fall back and tossed them again, but never cut them. He watched himself being watched the way women do.

In the times between the times when he hated himself, he was proud of his kindnesses. That morning his girlfriend Lydia had texted him: *You are a selfish piece of shit*, and the bluntness of the accusation made him feel defensive. He loved the feeling of being the right person at the right time. That month already he'd spent an afternoon helping a blind lady beg passers-by for change, so she could get a cab to the hospital. He'd have paid himself, but he only had £20 in his account and wanted to spend it on hash. It turned out she'd only been pretending to be blind, anyway, and this made him laugh but also feel sheepish. The week before that he'd met a guy in a wheelchair who'd asked to be pushed to the post office on Hendon High Road. Afterwards, they'd shared a box of twenty McNuggets, and the man showed him a video on his phone about the dangers of vaccines.

"Hmm," Eddie had said, unconvinced either way. He'd listened placidly to the earnest, angry lecture. He didn't have many strong convictions, but he admired those who did.

You are a selfish piece of shit, Lydia had written; the words kept creeping back to him, unbidden, and to stave off guilt he made a mental list of all the ways that she was selfish too. They'd been going out for seven months, and he was only just starting to feel resentful of certain things: the way she'd made a project of him, insistent on improving his wardrobe and diet in the same way she optimised every facet of her own life. The smugness with which she'd introduced him to her visibly horrified parents, whispering to him afterwards, "I've never dated a mixed-race boy before, sorry if they were weird."

But resentment never made Eddie feel any better. He didn't have the stamina for it. Eddie was the type to try and let bad feelings wash over him and dissipate. He didn't like to hold grudges or keep anger pinched in his chest. If something hurt, his attitude was, walk it off.

He was half-drunk and sleepy, now, strolling home from the park. The day had been hot, and he'd spent it playing football and drinking beer with some guys from school. He'd been trying to walk off his hurt, and hadn't wholly managed it, maybe because the hurt wasn't his alone: it was Lydia's, she was pregnant. He hadn't been able to think of what to say when she'd texted him the news last night, so he hadn't said anything, just gone to bed. This morning there'd been several missed calls, and the allegation, *you are a selfish* – no. Stop. He interrupted the thought, turned his face instinctively to the sun, and its warmth was grounding. He imitated the movements of a carefree person. He let his arms swing loose and gangly. He rolled his chewing gum into a perfect ball with his tongue and shot it like a bullet from his mouth. He watched it arc through the air and disappear into a hedge with a little shiver of leaves.

As a father, Eddie would be playful and attentive, he thought. Indulgent, even. His own father had dipped in and out of his childhood, interacting with the person he intended his son to become, rather than with the goofy boy he had. When he visited, he'd grill Eddie on current affairs. He was scathing of any hint of immaturity. Cold and cutting and disinterested. Eddie knew already that he would be different. Just, not yet. Not with *this* child. *You are a selfish piece of shit* – well, fuck her, if that's what she thought! He came upon a rock on the pavement and kicked it in satisfying punctuation of the word *fuck*; when he caught up to the rock he kicked it again, and this time it skidded to a halt at the feet of a dog.

What?

But, yes, there she was: sweet, coarse-furred beast, alone and padding around sort of aimlessly, between cars and up into the front gardens of the semi-detached Victorians to sniff at grubby rosebushes. The road was residential and empty and would have been quiet if it weren't barnacle-clamped to the edge of the North Circular. Instead, the engine buzz of passing cars frittered outwards and made the road hum. The houses were sooty from exhaust fumes.

Eddie stopped.

"Are you lost?" he called. The dog was a German Shephard; eventually he'd learn that her owners were a friendly Polish couple who worked full-time and left her howling and headbutting the bay windows all day. He never found out how she got loose. "Where are you supposed to be?"

Eddie didn't know about dogs, he'd never had one. He only knew the pleasant – paternal? – urge to protect things smaller and softer than himself. His mother was frightened of all animals, regardless of size. Even when he was small, she'd clutched at him anxiously whenever one came too close.

He kept a steady distance now, following as the dog snuffled along, wet snout to the ground. She paused once at the base of a lamppost and bent her hind legs meekly to squeeze out a shit. Eddie knew that she knew he was behind her. She made a game of it – she'd dart behind a car or run out into the road, and he'd have to jog to keep up.

He was sweaty and panting by the time he looked up and noticed a man, standing in the front doorway of one of the sooty houses, watching him. The man was short and dark-skinned and dressed in a t-shirt and basketball shorts that made his legs seem stumpy. His age was ambiguous, but only because all decades over forty blurred irrelevantly together in Eddie's mind. Eddie smiled at the man. Eddie had a good-guy smile, people said. It opened up his whole bright face specifically to *you*. "Just like your father's," his mother would say, suspiciously; she was always watchful for signs he might be turning into the other bad men she'd known.

"Is this your dog?" Eddie said to the short man.

"No," the man said, smiling back. His voice had a slightly mocking, flirtatious tone that made it seem like he might be joking, but the dog trotted confidently through his open front door, and he said, seriously this time, "No, I – this isn't my dog."

He had tried, Eddie saw, for bravado, but was helplessly awkward. "Maybe you could call the RSPCA?" said Eddie.

"Of course," said the man. "You must be tired after all that running around. Come in for a drink?"

You could offer Eddie things like this. That big kind smile encouraged braveness, spontaneity; you could see in his face that he wouldn't shut you down.

The decor of the short man's living room was lavish and clunky. Black leather sofas, a glass-top coffee table, a gargantuan flatscreen TV mounted to one wall. A deep crack spanning half the ceiling like a scruffy bolt of lightning. Eddie folded into sitting position on the edge of a sofa, a man-sized concertina, and his bony knees pointed straight up. The sofa had no feet, so it was an inch or so too short to be comfortable. Eddie's torso disappeared behind the height of his bent legs. His shell tracksuit bottoms strained at the seams. He was several beers deep from his day at the park and already pleasantly tipsy. The dog padded in a circle of eight in front of him, and slumped onto her belly, and looked up at him, and he scratched behind her ears. He saw that the tag on her collar had no phone number, but a name engraved in silver: JANE. His phone buzzed twice sharply, and he glanced at it: *Eddie???*

Of course, he was going to reply, but he could only gather his thoughts very slowly. Before today, Lydia had always held him at a distance. She'd been funny and cool and emotionally mysterious. They'd talked about babies once, just for fun, as a thought experiment, nose-to-nose after they'd crawled into bed still pinging at sunrise.

"I'd be the mean one," said Lydia. "I'd do the disciplining."

"I'd shower them with love," said Eddie.

"No, shower *me* with love!" said Lydia, rolling onto her back, like a puppy demanding belly rubs. But even then, somehow, she'd been ironic and in control.

* * *

The short man seated himself opposite Eddie in an armchair that made him miniature. His basketball shorts rode up a little and the leather seat squeaked against the backs of his bare thighs. At Eddie's feet, Jane thumped her tail against the bright cream carpet, which he saw was dotted with tiny food stains. Eddie leaned in, held Jane's face in both his hands, kissed her snout and the top of her head. He tried to focus on her, and this moment. This was a pleasant, low-stakes mystery. A gentle but unexpected shift in the direction of the day. A sour mood had been encroaching on him, and then – she appeared! What could she be except a reminder that things should be fun and easy? A chance to do a small good thing and enjoy the small good feeling that came with it?

"What's your name?" he said to the short man, with a new conviction to let himself be distracted.

The man was called Konwani, and when he called the RSPCA, he held his phone at a slight distance from his cheek, afraid to dirty either the screen or his face, Eddie couldn't tell. He stared at the wall behind Eddie's head and carefully recited his address. Eddie took note – curiously, without disdain – of Konwani's ragged hairline, and the firm curve of his calves, and the dry white skin that veined his bare heels. This man was uncle through to his core. He had the energy of a bullied maths teacher.

The phone call ended and Konwani leapt up to grab a six-pack from the kitchen. He turned on the too-big TV and muted it, so the images flashed distractingly in the background. In one corner of the room was an expensive-looking exercise bike, and Eddie imagined him pumping his little legs, sweat streaming from his temple, eyes fixed on the HD screen.

"Do you study?" Konwani asked, and Eddie told him yes, kind of; he'd just finished his A-Levels, and now these summer months (though they rolled towards Results Day) had taken on the sweet sheen of infinite freedom. Eddie felt wildly, recklessly untethered. At parties he was singled out and seduced by every bassline. He'd never been so aware of the blissful tingle of sun on skin. He couldn't get over the rich pleasure of all this unstructured sleeping and eating and texting the group chat to see who was free to chill at the park. But, more than this: he'd finally come unstuck from those dreary, mechanical interactions that seven years in the same institution had sunk him into. He'd become suddenly aware that the people he knew so far were only a fraction of the people he'd know his whole life, and each new person might propel further change, might be an entry point into some kind of adventure. Like this. Like now. He beamed at Konwani, who looked nervously at the ground.

Lydia disapproved of Eddie's attitude, of course. Her own future was an ambitious sequence of goals and projections that she marched doggedly towards. She was the opposite of Eddie's mother, who'd long ago resigned herself to life's disappointments. Eddie's mother had raised him with an attitude of helplessness. I am only one small woman, she seemed to think. What does it matter if I'm the one who birthed him, when there are forces so much bigger than my body that are shaping him? An absent black father, the vague evils of social media. Eddie hadn't inherited these fears, but his personality had grown out of them. He figured, the future was massive and inevitable. Stressing out about it made no difference. He would open himself up to everything and see what happened.

"You want to try some Malawi vodka?" Konwani said. He leapt up and fussed and clinked and sloshed at his liquor cabinet, returned with two slopping shot glasses and a bottle tucked under his armpit. They drank first to the dog, and then to their health, and then – at Konwani's suggestion – to Eddie's education and future prosperity. After each shot, they grimaced and smiled at each other. On the muted TV, one episode of South Park ended and another one began.

Eddie rambled cheerfully, but he didn't think to ask any questions, so they often lapsed into silence, and Konwani looked stricken with panic each time this happened, picking up his beer can and putting it down without sipping from it. He seemed, in the way he moved, hyper-aware of the edges of things, and where those things should be in relation to one another – as if he'd once been much larger and wasn't sure anymore of the distance between himself and his surroundings.

"You like music?" he asked.

"Yeah, definitely, I love it," said Eddie. Music *shaped* him, he'd have said, if he could find a less clichéd way of expressing the sentiment. "I'm in a band, me and some mates – it's like, kind of indie, kind of psychedelic rock. Like, Arctic Monkeys meets Tame Impala? I play bass. You should come to a gig some time."

Konwani seemed taken aback at the suggestion.

"Oh yes," he said. "Oh, I'd like that very much."

Eddie watched this, and watched Konwani's earnest eyes, and tried to measure the texture of their want. Eddie was a summer baby – he had no older brother and few black friends to borrow ID from; almost everyone in his year had turned eighteen already, and on nights out he told bouncer after bouncer that, shit, he'd left his driver's licence at home, would they let him in just this once? He knew that to be broad and firm was to make girls his age feel petite. The top of Lydia's shoulders tucked neatly into his armpit when she leaned against him. He knew she loved the image of the two of them (her taut blonde frame, his loping shaggy warmth); he felt her come alive when they were out in public together. He was used to straining to make himself less child, but somehow Konwani made his boyishness feel powerful. His own young body treated carelessly was still more lovely than this sculpted middle-aged man's.

Jane licked his hands industriously, over and over; in the rhythm of it he heard *I like you I like you I like you*. She leaned her full body weight against him, and he felt the comfort of a swaddled baby.

The doorbell rang, and Eddie checked his phone and realised whole hours had passed. He gulped his beer and unfurled from the sofa and swayed on his feet, drunker than he'd known himself to be a moment ago. He wondered, suddenly, if he should've just taken Jane home with him and asked his mother if they could keep her. Jane would have loved him unconditionally, he thought, and that kind of love might change him profoundly. But it was too late for this. The RSPCA volunteer was a grey-haired, dog-fluent woman in a practical fleece, and Jane followed her happily into the back of a van. Eddie and Konwani waved goodbye to her at the front door, and then she was gone, and the silence gaped between them.

*　*　*

Months later, strolling down the same sooty road, Eddie would see Jane again; this time with her owner, safely attached to a lead but straining against it, eyes fixed on a fat squirrel that froze against the flank of a tree. The whole scene made Eddie boundlessly happy, but when he crouched to pet her, she was aloof. She ducked out from his embrace. She was impatient. Her owner was apologetic – "She's a bit shy with strangers" – and Eddie was embarrassed at how much this stung.

"I need a smoke," said Eddie, now, in the doorway with Konwani. He pulled his tobacco from his back pocket and rolled a baggy cigarette with clumsy, too-long fingers. It was somehow night-time, and he was drunk, and the lampposts lit the houses in a soft orange glow.

He texted his mother: *At a friend's* and she replied, within seconds, with *Are you staying out?* and then, not waiting for his response: *DENTIST 9AM*. He realised this meant she'd probably been waiting by her phone, and he'd forgotten that she'd have made dinner for them both. The upstairs neighbours would probably be fighting, and even if she turned the TV volume up there'd be muffled bumps that kept her on edge. He felt a creeping shame and tried to catch the feeling before it spiralled into something that couldn't be contained, but already he was thinking about Lydia, and how she'd only ever showed her vulnerabilities in brief and unexpected glimpses, and Eddie had never quite managed to catch them in his stride and comfort her. A more intuitive person might learn to read the signs, like rippling water before a tsunami or glazed eyes at the onset of a seizure, but around her – around girls in general – Eddie became slow and self-absorbed. By the time he'd noticed her cautious exposure of weakness, she'd have snapped back shut. She texted him: *Eddie, please*, and now Konwani was turning back into the house, and Eddie was following him.

The living room felt much darker now. In a movement too awkward to have been spontaneous, Konwani sat next to Eddie on the sofa, and without the coffee table to keep polite distance between them, their legs bumped together. Eddie stiffened. He felt Konwani's wheedling eagerness, for the first time, as something with a life of its own, something forceful and beyond manipulation.

"You're a smart boy," Konwani said. "A good boy."

Eddie wriggled in protest at *boy*. The night had become too much, the feeling in his chest was too much, he couldn't describe it beyond its too-muchness.

"I've lived here fourteen years," Konwani was saying. "*Fourteen years* and still a bachelor! My God, my mother suffers. Every time I call to tell her about this or that promotion it's 'when will there be grandchildren?'"

"Oh wow," said Eddie, "oh man," and his head spun wildly, and he was only half-listening, and it didn't even matter – Konwani seemed not to need his participation anymore. He told rambling anecdotes that bled into one another. His voice grew louder as though he were trying to shout over himself.

"We should party," he declared. The timidity in his little round face was gone, and though Eddie's vision was too blurred to see the movement, he felt an arm snake around his shoulders, hot breath on his cheek. "You like to party, don't you?"

"I have a girlfriend," said Eddie. "I need to close my eyes."

He tried to rest his forearms on his towering knees and his left arm missed and dipped between his legs.

"Whoops," he said. He feared that he might be sick, and he wasn't sure he could walk far enough to do this in private. His eyes felt weighted, his head lolled, the room faded. When it sharpened again, seconds later, there was the sensation of one hand firm at the back of his neck, another clumsily fumbling at his waistband and then, giving up, yanking and squeezing through his tracksuit trousers. Eddie was flaccid and pitiful.

"What the *fuck*?" It took all his strength to drag himself fully into consciousness. His voice broke and squeaked, which happened still sometimes. He pushed himself upright and squared his shoulders, which he did when he was frightened, to show how much space he took up. "Wingspan of an albatross!" his mother sometimes exclaimed, in disbelief, prodding him as though he'd just now appeared this way, fully-formed. "I gave birth to that!"

The hand at his crotch jerked away, and Eddie blinked fuzzily at the blur of Konwani's junk scooped back into his underpants – an undignified flash of wrinkled ball-sack – and Konwani said, "no no no no don't get me wrong, don't worry, this is how I play with my little brothers back home, don't misunderstand me –"

Konwani's erection poked shily at the fabric of his basketball shorts and he tried with shaking hands to flatten the bulge.

"I'm not your little brother," Eddie said, scrabbling for his shoes, his phone. He stumbled towards the front door.

Konwani was frantic. He said, "Please don't go. They would kill me in my country. Please don't leave like this."

He looked close to tears, and Eddie despised himself with sudden blinding intensity.

* * *

Before Lydia, Eddie had gorged himself on girls. Each one had dazzled and consumed him briefly, and he would binge on her until he used up all his wonder and turned indifferent. He hadn't really seen this as a moral failing, because he had no control over the attraction. He presumed it was biological or evolutionary or something; that attention was a finite resource, and once you'd used up all your feelings for one person, all you could do was tap another source.

He moved mechanically towards home. The cold air sobered him. He had the sense that he wasn't moving forwards, but in some huge inevitable circle. He could only hear his own footsteps and the soft *whoosh* of cars from the nearby motorway, just out of sight. He called Lydia.

"I'm sorry," he said, when she answered. "My brain's fucked, I just needed some space to like…"

He waited for a good ending to the sentence to slot into place. There was only the long, slow intake of breath from Lydia's end, like she was steadying herself.

"You know what's so fucked up about this?" she said. "I don't even want your fucking baby."

He winced. He wasn't sure how to respond. His brain was moving too slowly.

"I'm obviously getting rid of it. You don't have to worry. I literally just wanted you to be there."

"Yeah, no, of course," said Eddie, pathetically. "I'm sorry. I just needed a minute to get my head around it. I'll be there. I'll –"

"No. Don't be there. Fuck you," said Lydia. "I don't know why I thought I needed anything from you."

She hung up. Eddie thought he'd feel more guilt, but there was only a brief rush of relief, then numbness.

The lights were all off by the time he reached home. The stairs seemed insurmountable, so he collapsed onto the sofa, fully clothed, and his mother woke him in the morning, twenty minutes before he had to leave for the dentist.

"I'll join you," she said. "We can get breakfast afterwards."

Normally, if he found himself too drunk to clean his teeth before bed, he'd make up for it by brushing three or four times over the course of the next day, but there was no time now, so he shoved a bottle of mouthwash in his jacket pocket and gargled and spat into a puddle as they walked along the high street. His mother grimaced at this.

For a long time, they walked in silence. Her footsteps fell in little skips to keep up with his stride. They both breathed the way you do on the brink of a thing you can't quite say.

"Eddie," said his mother, eventually. Her voice was cautious. "All this drinking and staying out – I mean, I know you've finished your exams, but –"

"I know, Mum," said Eddie. He was a patient person, mostly, but he was impatient with her.

"It's just –"

"Mum, I *know*," said Eddie.

He slowed his pace as the hill steepened, so his mother could catch her breath. She was too tiny to look after him. Her fringe was long and wispy and made her seem girlish. Once a month, Eddie helped paint her grey roots honey-blonde with box dye from Boots.

"Your father," said Eddie's mother, hesitantly, as if she weren't saying this for the thousandth time. "When we were young – you never saw a man so full of *potential*."

Eddie was gassy and sour and cavernously sad.

"I just keep thinking – the way he hurt himself, and the people around him," said his mother. "He could have done great things, and instead he's done so much harm. And I see so much of him in you."

This completed, within Eddie, a deep, familiar, clunking shift of gears. A move from a fierce sense of his own inherent goodness to a vitriolic self-loathing. He switched between these two feelings endlessly, sometimes back and forth and back again in a single day. Neither extreme moved him from the centre of his own universe.

He thought: his mother was right. He'd treated Lydia like shit. And last night, in Konwani's living room, he'd thought himself scared and helpless. He'd felt out of his depth. But he held power over people, he knew this about himself. Maybe that whole time he'd been powerful. He was strong and seedy and manipulative, he told himself. He was nothing so innocent as a boy.

* * *

He was late to his dentist appointment, and the nurse was curt and ushered him in without introducing herself, and the dentist smiled absent-mindedly, towards him but not quite at him. Eddie leaned back in the chair and knew there was gunk from yesterday's meals jammed in his gums, but he couldn't bring himself to care. He spread his dry lips and they cracked in the corners. The nurse stood poised with a little hose that sucked up the spit pooling under his tongue. The dentist, Dr Pitt, bent close, and the little metal stick he wielded made sharp tinny *tick tick tick*s against Eddie's teeth. His voice hummed in cryptic dental code, and he spoke the numbers rhythmically ("two one, two two"), and the buzz from his Adam's apple so close made Eddie's own throat suddenly constrict.

His mind lurched back to Konwani's hot dry hand edging towards his crotch, and he felt again the dread settling in his gut like some rancid liquid. Once on a damp black winter evening, walking alone through the park, a group of older boys had closed in on him, and he'd known with piercing clarity that they were going to beat the shit out of him, and though there must have been a point at which he could have stopped this from happening – by taking a different route, maybe, or starting the journey earlier – he'd let that moment slip by unnoticed, and now he could only resign himself to something brutal and inevitable. Somehow, with Konwani, he'd found himself in that hollow space he feared the most: where it was already too late to prevent the bad thing about to happen.

Now, reclined in Dr Pitt's chair, he forced his mind backwards. He fixed his thoughts on Jane, panting contentedly at his feet, and the sun outside still only on the brink of setting. He fixed on Konwani, opposite him in the big black armchair, not yet close enough to reach out and touch. Eddie fixed on that sweet surge of power he'd shimmered with as he felt himself framed by Konwani's gaze. In that moment, he'd been bright unfractured spectacle. He'd been total and yearned for.

The nurse turned to type something into the computer, and then it was just Eddie and Dr Pitt, and their faces were inches apart. On impulse, Eddie ran his tongue along the latex index finger that probed the inside of his cheek. It had a tangy plastic taste. He closed his lips around it and sucked. He looked into Dr Pitt's eyes – first blank, then panicked – for a long second before the finger pulled free, and it made a sloppy smacking sound that made Eddie laugh and dribble a little. His chest swelled with the kind of power a child has, total and meaningless. He waited to see what would happen next. He'd opened up a whole new spectrum of possibilities. It could be anything.

ANDREW DE SILVA

Cincinnati

"You should play Cincinnati," Thump said to Ryan one early June night as they knocked tennis balls against their pockmarked garage door. On other driveways attached to other houses on the cul-de-sac, kids played street hockey and rode bikes before their moms called them in for showers.

"I'd crush it," Ryan said. "Federer has pretty-boy hair, always stroking it out of his face."

"I'm serious," Thump said. She was set up to his left and hitting crosscourt backhands, sending them off the proper deflection point to reach her uncle's forehand. "You might not win, but you could do some damage."

"And Rafa's shorts stick to his crack," Ryan said. It was warm and the mosquitoes were out. They had one of those citrus-smelling tiki torches lit upwind, at the basketball hoop. "That's why all the tugging."

"Grandpa can stay with me for the week," she said. "I'll be okay."

"Ivan Ljubicic is a vampire accountant."

"You're not taking me serious," she said.

The kids from North Arlington were pushing Ryan, too, their assistant coach who could hit volleys behind his back and chase down lobs with tweeners. He still had it, they said, bookmarking old Youtube clips on the school computers. He could definitely still win. Ryan would smile at them and say "maybe," because they didn't know a thing.

"I would, honey," he said to his niece, curling a forehand. Last summer, on the week of the Lexington Challenger, Thump had bombed out of JCC sleepover camp on her first sobbing night. "But you know."

She smacked the ball too hard and high. It skidded over the roofline, barely missing the satellite dish.

Ryan looked at her as hard as he dared, but the truth is he was still scared of her, this nine-year old, of what her mood meant for the rest of their night. Four years together and still no clue what he was doing. He pointed his finger to the sideyard. She took his racquet from his hand and bounced the frame against her strings, then bounced her frame against his strings, gauging both stringbeds. "I'm telling you," she said. "If you get in shape. And cut these strings, they're dead as dodos." She gave the sticks back and disappeared around the house for the ball.

Adolescence—that was the musk she'd gotten from the older kids, hanging out at the high school matches. Certain and horizonless. But she was right about the strings. They'd been nine weeks in tension and were dead as dodos.

Later that evening he let her snip the racquets with her school scissors. He dragged out his stringing machine while they watched TV and ate Oreos out of the package. When Thump went to bed he called the Western & Southern office. "They say I can still do some damage," he said to the voicemail, and within the week, yes, Cincinnati. People in the Midwest had not forgotten.

*　　*　　*

All July he waited for Thump to renege but she never did, and Grandpa Lou showed up on the morning of August 13 with a box of his crap, prepared to stay until Ryan lost his match and drove his Dakota the five hours back to Chicago. They were all out on the lawn saying their goodbyes when Thump gave Ryan the scissors.

"Stringing's free if you're entered," she said. "And leave the truck at the hotel and take the courtesy shuttle. So you don't have to think about the road before a match."

"Done and done," Ryan said.

"There's a hospitality tent. I bet it'll have healthy stuff—carrots, burgers with mushrooms instead of meat and stuff. It's free too," she said, handing him a Ziploc bag.

"You working for the tournament?" Grandpa Lou asked her, laughing his big laugh. That's why everyone called him Big Lou—everything about him larger than life.

"It's in the player packet," she said. "It's a PDF you download right from the site."

Kids liked to know facts at this age, Ryan had noticed. The different categories of clouds and the web of animal species. To study maps and announce where they were going. In this way she was still a child; he kissed her on her child's forehead.

"Call me," he said to her.

He got on I-65 in Gary and routed southeast through Indianapolis, and like that, in one morning, he'd passed through the membrane that had separated Ryan Schwartz from Blood Schwartz for almost fifteen hundred days. He cranked some Smashing Pumpkins, felt the adrenaline or endorphins or whatever those chemicals were; he drummed the steering wheel until it shuddered.

* * *

Cincy was sticky, humid, made him wish he'd thinned his chest hair with the #2 attachment on the clippers. He wandered until he found the main draw. Roddick. Safin. Federer. Davydenko. Baghdatis. People checked websites for draws these days, but most tourneys still had one giant version in the central concourse, gloriously analog, names on white wooden rectangles slotted into the brackets. Nadal was here, Nalbandian and Blake, and in the final quarter of the 2006 Western and Southern Financial Group Masters Men's Draw, in a first-round matchup with #14 seed Tommy Haas: (WC) Ryan Schwartz. He took his camera out of his racquet bag and snapped a picture.

He boarded the shuttle to the hotel fifteen minutes early and had to pretend to mind his business, checking his phone for Thump and Big Lou as people filed on. There were coaches (fit, older) and players (fit, younger) and trainers (fit to the point of sinew, and offputting), all sweaty but emitting a certain energy that came standard with a tournament's opening days, when no one had lost yet, when every path through the brackets seemed possible.

"Blood!" said an Eastern-bloc accent, making its way down the shuttle aisle with open arms. Ivo Hradek. "I've seen a ghost!" Ivo said.

They hugged deep and tight. He'd known the Czech since forever, since the academy.

"Are you back?" Ivo asked. "Did you qualify?"

"Wild card, baby," Ryan said. The backdoor; the grace of the director; the carrot they gave to players who were too interesting to leave out.

"Tell me things," Ivo said, sliding in next to him. "Where do you live? What's your life?"

"What *is* my life…"

"You look happy to be here. That makes me happy."

"You know what?" Ryan said. "I am."

"Good," Ivo said, bright with sincerity. "And your tennis, it's good? Diving your volleys and skinning your knees?"

"Less of that, now." Ryan said.

"And what else? Your wrist? Your brother?"

Ryan forgot that Dan and Ivo had met—that anyone would know his brother here.

"Dan the hockey man," Ivo said.

Ryan at fourteen: stuck in Florida with the foreign kids over Thanksgiving, when mom and Big Lou couldn't afford to fly him back. Dan, teaching them to mix vodka with Sprite at the Wendy's fountain machine. Ryan hadn't wanted to lose the memory of his brother, necessarily, but if you didn't fight to hold on, time would turn absence into blankness, and whether that was tragic or some natural form of pain management depended on who the person was and what they'd done to you.

"He's been hard to pin down," Ryan said. "But he'd be glad to know I saw you."

The conversation deflated a little, and after some throwaway reminiscing about their comrades from Bradenton, about the trials of 1996, it tapered to quiet sitting. But it felt good to sit next to an old friend all the same, elbows grazing as the shuttle plowed through summertime American streets. Ryan sensed Ivo felt the same way. Sometimes it was enough to know that the prior part of their lives had really happened.

* * *

He had tried to tell Thump a hundred times the first year, but Ryan could not do it in the driveway or on the way to school. Every routine place in their lives suddenly felt sacred, like it needed to be protected for future use. So that spring, in 2004, he took her on a road trip to Cedar Point, the amusement park on the banks of Lake Erie. They ate broccoli cheddar breadbowls from Panera off the turnpike. They camped at Lighthouse Point in the shadows of a clacking wooden coaster. Thump had strong fingers and they hurt when they dug into his arm on the rides; more than once he had to redirect her to the grip bar.

On the second day he built up the nerve. They were braced for the Corkscrew, buckled-in and captive. When he'd downloaded the forms from the Cook County website, he'd read the dreadful scripts online:

"Hi (child's name), I'd like to talk about our family today. Do you know what a guardian is?"

"It's like an extra mommy or daddy. Another adult who loves you and will take care of you."

"We're making a new family, but we're keeping so many parts of the old one. We'll celebrate the same holidays and eat your same favorite foods."

But he couldn't use any of it, because right then Thump saw Dan, two cars in front of them on the coaster. It happened a couple times a month:

she would spot some big guy in a crowd and point, sometimes run up and tug on his shirt, convinced she'd found him. It was devastating but also kind of beautiful that she thought the world so contained—that her dad, all this time, had gotten lost buying athletic socks at the drug store or ordering breadsticks at the chain restaurant in the parking lot of the Target. And the truth is Ryan did it too, spotting Phantom Dans all over Chicago.

When the ride ended and the Corkscrew harness released, Thump scurried down the exit walk, far enough ahead so that she could turn back and see the man head-on, this man who looked nothing like her father but in the vaguest profile.

*   *   *

When Ryan couldn't tell her there, he went to the only place he could. Found the address for Sandusky High School and drove over the next morning, before the amusement park opened. The row of courts shared a fence with two blacktop basketball courts. Dew slicked the white paint on the lines. Parks and high schools were the centers of free tennis in America—Big Lou had been a fixture in late-eighties Chicago, obsessed with Andre Agassi and the way Andre's father had constructed him. Big Lou, feeding Ryan balls from a rusty white hopper and giving the advice he read in books. A constellation of Ryan's life could be traced across so many public tennis courts.

Ryan and Thump stood in opposite service boxes and warmed up with the beach ball. The ball made a pleasing smack as it hit the stringbeds.

"Control that follow-through," he said. "Strokes, not slaps."

Thump wore a fleece that doubled her width. Her hair was a rat's nest on the right side of her face—she twirled it in her car seat, on drives, like a mindless tic.

"Good. Watch the ball, not me. Good. Now bounces."

"How many?"

"Twenty."

She bounced the ball on her racquet, up and down, up and down, hyper-focused, unaware of her feet pinwheeling drunkenly around the service box in chase.

"Now for real," he said, switching the beach ball for a modified Penn. Off-the-rack tennis balls were too hard, too heavy and bouncy for little kids to control, and it discouraged them from the game. Ryan punctured the balls with a sewing needle to depressurize them, the way Big Lou had. "Twenty more," he said.

She bounced, pinwheeled, reset, bounced. His breathing went double-speed.

"Hey Kit," he said, using the name her parents gave her. The one that meant *listen*. "Do you know what a guardian is?"

She kept counting her bounces in a hoarse whisper.

"A guardian is like an extra mom or dad. Another adult who loves you and will take care of you."

"*Ten. Eleven*," she said.

"You know, just stop and listen. I have something to tell you. I don't think your dad is in Chicago anymore."

"*Sixteen. Seventeen.*"

"Stop bouncing, Kit. I don't think he's coming back. I don't think we can plan like he's coming back.

"I think it's just you and me in that house. But that's good, right? That's a good old family."

She got past twenty, kept going.

"We're best buds, and I think it will be enough."

She said nothing, *thirty* and then *thirty-one* and finally he snatched her bouncing ball right out of the air. He couldn't read her; it was impossible he couldn't read a six-year old, they were like two intellectual steps past a golden retriever at this age but he couldn't.

She stalked to the bench between courts and grabbed the Penn can and tipped another ball into her hand. "Can we please stop TALKING ABOUT THIS," she said, running to the next court to continue her bouncing with a giant-ass buffer between them.

The sun made Ryan squint; he could feel the folds of his crow's feet compressing around his eyes. Gulls from the lake picked through the high school dumpster. But what should he have expected, from any of it? They'd only ever trained him to swing a stick inside a rectangle.

* * *

He and Ivo carb-loaded dinner together at a Macaroni Grill. After, Ryan locked himself into his hotel room, waiting for Thumper to call. He flipped through the channels without her whining for cartoons, made angels across the bed's perfect hotel sheets. He visualized his hitting patterns against Haas, body-serving the German's graceful backhand so he couldn't wind up for a cut.

He ate a pack of Sour Patch Kids from the small zippered pouch on the right side of his racquet bag. He kissed the tips of his index and middle fingers and tapped Thump's scissors for good luck, then cut the strings on three of his six sticks. He regripped them and picked yellow fluff from their bumpers. It was only 8:48pm.

He drank water until his pee ran super-clear. He texted a number that texted him back the weather. More humidity. Cincinnati wasn't the Midwest, really—it was Kentucky, and Kentucky was a whole other thing.

He called Thump and got no answer. He called Big Lou and same. Finally he went down to the hotel's Business Center to use a computer, to see if there had been any fires, or murders, in the west suburbs of Chicago. A player from Australia Skyped with his girlfriend on the computer next to him. The guy's web-cam was fitted snugly, cleverly, into the hollow shell of a tennis ball. The internet told Ryan there had been no fires or murders, but only in the hours before dawn did he find a racing and unpleasant sleep.

*   *   *

On the practice court the next morning he faced the net and took his service position and bounced the ball between his legs, from outside his left thigh to inside like a point guard's dribble, catching it only long enough to send it back to the outside and give one final bounce at the toe. He held the ball lightly in his left fingers, palm open and aligned with his right wrist, both arms now in unison as he rocked forward, rocked back. At the terminal point of this backward rocking he broke the union of his arms; the left arm arced forward to toss the ball while the right arm pulled backward to torque the racquet. As he released the ball he bent deeply at the knees, growing smaller and more coiled as the toss climbed into the sky, optic yellow felt against pale morning blue, the striker separating from the object to be struck—in this distance, all power was generated, and he reached the part in every service motion when the ball is at the very top of its ascent and gravity says *no sir this is where you stop* and the ball does seem to pause, and physics shut down, for one ripe moment.

He burst from bent knees toward it. The motion was calibrated so that he'd make contact ten feet above the court, the precise y-coordinate height reached by the explosive center of his racquet when added to the height of his fully extended elbow and pronated wrist, snapping into the universe with grim intent.

*   *   *

And that was Cincinnati. One serve, on a practice court, before the phone finally rang.

"Hey, when do you play?" Big Lou asked.

"Twenty minutes."

"I thought you'd be in warm-up. I thought I'd leave a message."

"What's up? She okay?"

"Nothing," Big Lou said. "It can wait. I meant for it to wait."

"Now I can't not think about it."

"You don't need to worry."

"We'll see."

"You don't."

"I won't," Ryan said.

"You gonna jam his backhand off the serve? Haas doesn't like ugly tennis. Play ugly tennis."

"Tell me, dad."

"Fine. But don't worry about it, on the court."

"TELL ME THE FUCKING THING."

Big Lou breathed heavy through the phone. "I think we're being followed."

Ryan rotated two balls in his palm, feeling for the one he liked best. "What do you mean?"

"Like 100% sure."

"What is *followed*?" Ryan said.

"Like someone got hired to do it."

"I don't know what you're telling me. It's not the Cold War, people aren't getting followed."

"A private eye, Ry. It's the Canadians."

The Canadians. Thump's family on her mom's side, her grandmother whining and tampering the whole four years. And Ryan should have been furious with the old woman, but it was with Thump, in that first flash, in that awful and honest burst from the soul. For having this happen to her. For existing at all. Ryan slipped his stick into the racquet bag and fished the car keys out of the pouch.

By the time he got to the truck his resentments had gotten right again in his head, the way they always did. The beautiful child; the degenerate brother; the terrible world. He stood on the white lines of the parking lot, next to the Dakota. Thinking it through. He zipped the keys back inside the racquet bag, and he walked away from the truck.

He showed his badge and re-entered the stadium grounds and found one of the normal bathrooms, for the spectators. Locked himself in a stall and took off his shoe and tried to kick his foot against the stall door as hard as he could. Couldn't do it. Human nature or whatever to pull back at the last second. So he started light and built up to it, swinging harder and harder, trying to jam the toes without breaking them. *Thwack, thwack,* but he couldn't. He pulled out his phone and called Ivo.

"No way," Ivo said when he got to the bathroom, staring at Ryan's foot resting on the sink.

"Please," Ryan said.

Ivo took the racquet but couldn't even cock it. "Just lie! You pulled a hamstring, or anything."

"Please, Ivo. It has to be real."

They stood there looking at each other in the tube-fluorescent light, and when it became clear Ivo really meant it, that he wouldn't swing, Ryan returned to the stall door and *thwack-thwacked* until he stubbed the bone real good, Ivo calling him a dumbass, a wildman, the whole time. Ryan limped a real limp out of the bathroom on a red and bulging toe. Ivo sighed and came over, let Ryan use him as a crutch. At the concourse they hugged their farewell. Ryan made for the hospitality tent alone, to stash some Danishes in the Ziploc.

On the drive home he turned the Pumpkins on the stereo. Loud, and louder, as he passed through the membrane again, as he felt Cincinnati closing up behind him. He tried to keep the truck under ninety.

*   *   *

He and Federer had once pooed next to each other in adjacent stalls. It was 1998 at the Orange Bowl in Miami, the most prestigious junior tournament in the world. Fed won the 18s that year over Guillermo Coria, Ryan lost to Dennis DeKlerk in the finals of the 16s, and their schedules had aligned all week. It was the thirty minutes before their mutual semi-finals and they were both in the bathroom taking nervous shits, butterfly-in-stomach shits. Ryan could tell it was Roger by his shoes. Kids were real good at memorizing each other's shoes.

The Swiss was no man of mystery even then, and neither was the brawny kid from Chicago. The people who needed to know about them already knew about them—the national federations and coaches and agents—because in elite tennis no one emerged from obscurity. A barely-scouted high school tight end from east bumfuck could end up an All-Pro tackle a decade later, that kind of thing happened. But no real tennis players played high school tennis, however much Ryan would have loved it, and no real tennis players incubated in the east bumfucks of the world for long. There were tracks, here, and you hopped on the trains early, and if you got lucky, and a bit anointed, your particular train disembarked in South Florida in December for the Orange Bowl pomp and circumstance, shadowing a kid who'd won the Boy's Singles and Doubles at Wimbledon five months earlier.

Ryan wondered if he should say something to Roger. *"Hey man, love the way you place your serve,"* but a person couldn't talk under a stall door to a stranger, because that was creepy. Instead he imagined how it might go:

"Thanks, Schwartz. Seen your name in the draw. Recognized those shoes."

"Aw shit, these beat-up things."

"They're real, you know?" Fed would say. *"You're real. Respect."*

Roger tapped his feet, like he was listening to a Discman or just remembering a song. That's another thing they could talk about. Ryan liked Rage for his fire-up—Dan had taught him to play angry, to hate his opponents, to want to destroy them and burn them to ashes like Vikings on the pillage—

"Hey," said the shoes from under the divider.

Ryan stopped breathing. Stopped thinking.

"Hey kid?" said the shoes.

"Yeah?"

"Help me out with some paper."

Holy crap.

Ryan rolled it out, kept slapping the roll and folding the unrolled slack in his hand so he had a beautiful accordion of toilet paper to offer Roger under the divider. Roger's fingertips appeared and took the accordion, and holy crap. Federer was great but he pulled his shorts down on top of his shoes like everyone else. Bitched about line calls like everyone else. Glared at his coaches and had a face full of surly pimples—they could both talk about their pimples.

Federer flushed first, left his stall first, and when Ryan came out the kid was preening a little, smoothing out those heavy Federer eyebrows and shaping his frosted hair in the locker room mirror. Bleach-blonde hair, like 'N Sync, like a proper late-nineties teenager. Ryan took the sink next to him, splashed water on his own face. He already had to go again—these nervous shits could compound forever with diminishing returns, and at some point you just had to clench up and grab your sticks and head out to the court for warm-ups.

Roger dried his hands carefully with the paper towel, looking directly at Ryan through the mirror.

"Good luck," he said.

"Thanks," Ryan said. "You too."

"Play like you play. Like a crazy motherfucker, you know?"

* * *

Traffic added two hours but Ryan eventually got home, took the racquet bag out of the bed of the truck. In the house Big Lou gave him one disappointed head-shake and moved on.

"The private eye's here," Big Lou said. "In the kitchen."

"The one following us?"

"The one I hired. The one following the one following us."

"Jesus, dad," Ryan said, walking behind. "Thump?"

"In her room. Headphones." Big Lou put his hands over his ears to mime it.

A woman sat at the kitchen table. She wasn't wearing a trench coat or a fedora or whatever clueless vision Ryan had of private eyes. Maybe fifty years old, jeans and gray running shoes. A tan like she'd spent August at the lake.

"This is Sheila," Big Lou said.

"You the tennis brother?" she asked Ryan.

"Yeah."

"It's the hockey one that's gone?"

Ryan held a finger up. He walked down the hallway, to the girl's room. She'd stopped searching for Dan two years ago, out in public. Now she hardly mentioned him at all. But still—she didn't need to hear this. Ryan could see through the angle of the door and the reflection off the mirrored closet that she was on her DVD player. Still twirling her hair during every idle moment, no matter how much they worked on it. He retreated to the kitchen.

"Yeah," he said to Sheila. "It's the hockey one that's gone."

"Your guy is Jeff Garza," she said. "Hired by the grandma from Toronto, to see how Kit Schwartz was living."

Big Lou nodded while Sheila spoke. The man always knew odd-jobbers like this: guys who worked baggage claim at O'Hare, guys who fixed the elevators in the skyscrapers in the Loop.

"To see if it was on the up-and-up," Sheila said. "Or if Jeff could take some notes for Child Services. Take some photos. It's real typical."

"So what do we do?" Ryan asked. "We pressure him a little?"

She laughed.

"What?" Ryan said. He wanted them out of his house. To move this stupid drama along.

"The answer is, don't give him stuff to report," she said. "Feed her. Bathe her. Don't smoke crack near big picture windows."

"We can do that!" Big Lou said, grinning. He pulled three hundred-dollar bills from the sheath in his wallet and handed them to Ryan. "He's in the car out front."

"Me?" Ryan said, to which Big Lou said nothing—only a face, like it was the most obvious thing in the world.

Ryan slid his flip-flops over his socks until they wedged. He limped out the front door, to the private eye wearing the green t-shirt in the Honda CRV, and made the *roll-down-your-window* signal.

"Hey," Ryan said, cash between his thumb and fingers.

"Hey," the man said.

Ryan gave him the money. "So, you don't need to come by anymore."

"Sheila tell you the deal?"

"You know Sheila?"

"We're old friends. She recognized my car."

"No wiretap?" Ryan said. "Or whatever?"

"No," he said. "No wiretap."

When Ryan came back inside, Big Lou and Sheila were at the family room window, watching.

"So this is done?" Ryan said.

"Yeah, I mean," his dad said. "But you know."

"What?"

"Look at the house, Ry," his dad said, pointing to the brown grass, to the barren beds under the window. "Would it kill you to plant a shrub?"

* * *

That evening Ryan set Thump up with another DVD in her room. He got a bottle of white wine and a bag of Chessmen and turned on the tournament. Roger Federer vs. Paradorn Srichaphan. The elegant backhand, the ebb and then the flow.

Late in the first set, Thump came out and sat on the couch. She watched a few points. She spoke without taking her eyes from the television. "Was it because of me?"

"Naw," he said.

On the television, Federer bent a forehand passing shot from the doubles alley into the singles corner. He moved like he had antigravity in his shoes, like friction somehow relaxed around the cone of his body.

"There was a lady in the house," Thump said.

"That had nothing to do with it," he said.

"I know there was a lady."

"I busted my toe, Thumper," he said. He pulled off his sock. It looked worse than it felt—purple in the bruise, blood under the nail.

"Oh," she said, and he could see the relief in her. Could feel her feeling it. "Ouch," she said.

Ryan pulled the girl closer. Cozied her right up next to him, to prolong this little euphoria in his heart. Fed and Mirka would have a daughter one day and they'd have twenty au pairs for her, taking her to the pediatrician and clipping up her bangs and managing the troubles of her world. Fed sure as shit didn't know how to plant a shrub.

"You'll do another one?" she said. "When it heals?"

"Maybe," he said. "I don't know."

"There's a Challenger in Lubbock, in September."

He licked the residual cookie from the crowns of his molars. This time, she was looking straight at him.

"Lubbock," he said.

"Texas," she said.

They watched for a while more, ten or twenty minutes—televised tennis had a hypnotic quality, service holds and break points saved and service holds; shots of the players drinking Gatorade and finicking with their towels; the same financial-planning commercials playing on a loop, like the network could only get so many sponsors. Eventually Thump pulled the Chessmen bag to her side and folded the top.

"We'll see the highlights on ESPN.com," she said. "They have good highlights."

"They do," he said to the child.

She led him to the garage for their sticks, and they did the Indiana Jones trick where they pushed the button and hopped over the laser before the door closed on their backs. The neighborhood kids were out, playing their tag and their street hockey. Crickets and sprinklers. A Dairy Queen cup, soggy on the sewer grate.

He and Thump rallied into the twilight, judging the carom, the way the hinged segments of the garage gave an unpredictable bounce, the way the triangle of siding above the door played more live than the door itself. The floodlight came on on the timer, and they rallied for a little while more.

georgia campbell

digestible

Ingrid worked at the central table repairing a hole in Sir's mouth. Sir was one of the fish puppets used in advert bumpers for a children's TV channel. The other fish had more robust, plastic mouths, but Sir was only a soft monkfish and the puppeteer was rough with him. It was a running gag on the channel to have Sir rarely appear on the bumpers, but whenever he did, he looked older and had developed more injuries. Ingrid was always instructed to make Sir's stitches large and clumsy. This time, she had been asked to shear off some of his fin as well.

Mr Guratsky sat at the client table with two men from The Lois, a small theatre beneath a bowling alley. The two men sat far apart from each other but weaved their arms together to demonstrate what they wanted.

'All over the stage,' one of them said.

'Hanging off the stage, even.'

'And continuous, just as if they've been unravelled.'

Mr Guratsky was writing something. With his other hand he held up his face, cheeks spilling up and over his fingers.

'Yes. Right,' he said through his hand. 'As I say, this might work better if it were mechanical. To create the—rolls and pulses. For it to move by itself. And we don't do that here.'

'But we want something that feels organic, something where you can't always predict its movement.'

'And we imagine a mechanical intestine would be more expensive.'

Mr Guratsky nodded and made a few non-committal noises. 'It's just,' he began. 'Working out how to—you understand...'

Ingrid turned to the TV beside her. It was set up to be the first thing clients saw when they walked into the workshop. It cycled through different series segments that featured Mr Guratsky's puppets.

'Mr Guratsky,' Ingrid called out. 'You could make it like the sea anemone.'

'What did she say?' one of the men asked.

'Sea anemone,' Mr Guratsky mumbled behind his hand, and pointed to the TV.

73

The two men came and bent over to peer at the TV.

'It will have to cycle through again,' Ingrid said.

'Hm?'

'Just give it a second.'

One of the men was looking only at Sir, who had Ingrid's hand inside him. When the anemone appeared again, Ingrid quickly pointed to the screen with Sir.

'Like that,' she said. The clownfish puppet emerged from his anemone and approached the screen to speak to them. The TV was always on mute.

The men still couldn't understand her, and before she could explain the screen switched to another segment.

Mr Guratsky explained how he had made the limbs of the anemone with thick foam and a cavity inside, so numerous people could push their arms inside to make the anemone sway.

'So, it might be possible to do something similar with your intestines. We could try to make the cavity large enough for your actor, but with the foam sturdy enough that you won't see his outline.'

Throughout his explanation, the men stared at Ingrid and nodded along as if she were talking.

'That would be perfect,' one of them said.

They returned to Mr Guratsky, who put together a schedule for them and arranged a time for the actor to come in for a cavity fitting. Once he'd said goodbye to them at the door, he came over to Ingrid's station, drumming his hands to disguise how heavily he was leaning his weight on the table.

'Right, well...' he said. 'That was difficult to digest. Hah.'

He made it to the café next door just in time to be sick in their bathroom.

* * *

Mr Guratsky did not want to put Ingrid in charge of the intestines—she was still his apprentice and had never handled a job by herself before—but he was clearly indisposed and could not even work in the same vicinity as the red fabric. He instead cleared out the back room for Ingrid, and left for her the swatches he felt would work best.

'Just show whichever one you choose to the lady at *Scissors*,' he added. 'You'll need—it'll be on the sheet.'

He found her the client sheet the two men had filled in, but they'd given no measurements, only *Size: long*.

'Well,' he said, 'just use your better judgement.'

'Okay.'

Ingrid, once Mr Guratsky had left her room, picked up each of the swatches one at a time. He'd chosen a polished cotton, a metallic lame, organza and silk. Ingrid wrapped each swatch around her finger and made it crawl around her table like the men had described the creature's intestines on the stage.

To give her space, Mr Guratsky had stored his fat computer beneath the table. She crawled under and turned it on, using the top of her thigh to control the mouse. When she first searched for just *intestines*, there were only medical diagrams. *real intestines*. She put the computer to sleep and took her coat. She left behind the swatches. Mr Guratsky warned her that *Scissors* would not be open for another hour.

Further into the city was the meat market. She approached the glass case and stared until one of the men asked her what she was looking for.

'What sausages do you have?' she asked.

'Sausages?' he said, as if it were an odd request.

Ingrid nodded, and he directed her to the furthest right of the case. The sausages were sickly and lay on false grass in tight spirals.

'It's just meat,' the man said. Ingrid was sneering.

She was able to choose one in the end. It was the closest in colour to the images online. She took the paper bag and found a bench on the street. She put her hand inside the bag and ran her fingers along the coil and committed the sensation to memory. Of the swatches, it was closest to the silk, but she knew Mr Guratsky had put that there as a test; silk wasn't in the men's budget.

In a moment the coil was gone and the meat was all in her fist. She rubbed her fingers together to feel the roughness inside, with the smooth casing broken. She brought the bag to her mouth and pressed her tongue into a clod on her palm. She shivered and threw the bag into the road. When a car drove over it, immediately the skin of the bag was saturated and dark.

*　*　*

Scissors was arranged in such a way that you would not meet the sales assistants until you had traversed the entire array of fabrics. There was no hope if you needed help. You had to find your way through, and then the sales assistants would emerge in a dead end with shelves of buttons and accessories.

Ingrid passed through the tall columns of red fabric until it gradated into pink. She ran her fingers along the silk offerings. In the opposite aisle was the organza. She stretched her arms to feel the organza and silk at the same time, balled them in her fists. Further along she found a slick fabric. There was a graininess to it when she rubbed it between her fingers, but it looked almost wet, reflecting all the light. It would have been a sweet fabric for a child's raincoat. On a lower shelf, she found the same material in a muddier pink. She pulled it out, along with the organza, and found her way to the front.

*   *   *

Ingrid heard the actor arrive. Mr Guratsky was just leaving for the day, so he quickly ushered him into the backroom, where Ingrid was waiting with a tape measure.

'Hello', she said.

The actor slammed the door and shot his arms out to the side.

'Oh, this is always the worst part.' The tape measure unravelled. 'Don't even tell me the numbers.'

'I only need to measure your widest part—'

'*Oh*. I have a widest part.'

'So you don't get stuck in the cavity.'

When Ingrid approached with the tape measure, he shrank away and barricaded himself on the other side of the table.

'This is interesting,' he said, picking up the pink material. 'It's not latex, is it? I'm allergic.'

'I don't think it is.'

Ingrid tried to throw the tape around the actor's shoulders while he ran his palms along the fabric, but he was too tall and the tape caught in his hair. With one hand, he willingly lassoed himself by pulling it down to his neck. Ingrid set it into place around his shoulders.

'Hm. I suppose this would be my widest part. You could be measuring me for my birth.'

'I'll make it slightly larger than this so you can move your arms freely.'

'No, no,' he said, still with his hands on the fabric. 'Keep it tight.'

Ingrid moved back to her side of the table and made more notes than she needed to.

'My name's Mark,' he said.

'Ingrid.'

'Will you be there when we open?' he asked.

'Mr Guratsky and I aren't the best with horror.'

'Oh, it's not a horror. It's quite sad actually.'

digestible

From her side, she smoothed the material where it had folded over. She'd found it tended to keep any marks, and could not be ironed.

'I'm afraid I do feel that anything involving giant intestines must be a horror. And it all seems quite clichéd, all the gore and the monster.'

'He's not a monster. He's human. The thing is, they keep trying to kill him, but parts of him keep living. Is that not intriguing?'

His fingers were roaming beneath the material.

'No. There are plenty of stories about resilience,' Ingrid said. She put her hand underneath the material as well, but kept her palm flat against the table.

'That's not it, though. You're misunderstanding.'

'What is it about, then?'

'Why don't you come? Look at me. I promise it's not scary, alright? The scariest part is probably the intestines, and you made them, so you can't be scared of them.'

'Will there be audience participation?' Ingrid asked.

'Oh, of course.'

'Then I won't be in attendance.'

He smiled at her. When she lifted her head to look at him, he lurched forward. He tried to grab her hand, but she moved hers away at just the right moment. He tried again, but she took her other hand and brought it down hard on his fingers.

He did not flinch, but started to laugh, as did she.

'I knew you were going to do that,' Ingrid said.

'How?'

She shrugged.

*   *   *

Soon, the foam innards snaked the floor of the backroom. Ingrid stored her shoes on top of the computer to avoid damaging the foam.

She stepped between each coil to reach the door. Mr Guratsky had just returned with more foam for her when she opened the door to free the intestines.

'Going well?' he asked.

'I'm out of space. I'll need to spread—'

'No, they'll fit in your room.'

The wedge of foam barricaded Ingrid into the backroom.

'How will I breathe?'

He cut a whole well above his eye level, then pushed the foam further inside until Ingrid had enough to cut out the next two pieces. She threw them over her shoulders as she found her way back to the workbench.

The most laborious process was shaping the foam to be perfectly cylindrical. She and Mr Guratsky often spent hours trimming the smallest swells of foam to form puppets' bodies, but it would have taken Ingrid years to do the intestines in the same way. Instead, she used the large sewing scissors and spread the blades apart, holding one in her fist and using the other blade to shear along the length of the piece. Since it was so difficult to move around the room, she used her free hand to funnel the length of foam towards her. It was a similar procedure to scrape out the cavity for the actor, before gluing the two halves together and affixing the piece to the end of the long trail.

By the end of the day, she had almost depleted the second batch of foam and the intestines reached the middle of her thighs. The remaining foam still trapped her in the backroom. She had to tread carefully to the doorway, but she heard voices coming through the air hole Mr Guratsky had cut for her.

'... something you need?'

'Is she still in there?'

It was the actor. Ingrid dove into the foam and crawled into the end of the cavity. She wormed her way further inside, but stopped when she heard his voice again.

'I am here to save you, my love.'

She remained still.

'You're free.'

She felt him stepping clumsily through the coils.

'Where has my love gone? Oh, perhaps I will never find her.'

She was being pushed down. He was sitting on her. She let out a scream.

'Have I found her? Have I found her in time?'

Mark's voice reverberated around the cavity. He took hold of her ankle and pulled her to freedom.

Exhausted by the effort, he collapsed onto a length of foam. Ingrid lay on the coil beside him and looked towards the open doorway. He'd kicked in the barricade.

'How did you know I was there?' Ingrid asked.

'Where else would you've been hiding?'

'No, but how did you know I was *there*? In that part of the tube?'

'Ah. I just knew. Some things are very easy to know.'

Ingrid turned to him. He was already looking at her.

'What do you know about me?'

'Everything.'

'Even my thoughts?'

'I can see them right here.' He prodded her forehead and pretended to take something. He held it between his thumb and index. It was the size of a grape. 'They're all mine for the taking.'

'If my thoughts are yours, then yours are mine.'

'All yours.'

*   *   *

He came home with her on the train, where they surveyed the carriage and theorised which passengers would fit inside the intestines.

'Yes, they would fit,' he said. 'She would. And I think we'd be able to squeeze him into them. No for everyone else, though.'

'I thought the same.'

'Of course, they're only for me, aren't they?'

He looked tall inside her flat, with his shadow spread across the furniture.

*   *   *

The puppet took Ingrid another two weeks to complete. She was still not quite ready when the deadline arrived. The Lois needed it for their final dress rehearsal as soon as possible. In the end, intestines became so long that Ingrid had to overrule Mr Guratsky and commandeer the front room, forcing him to work from home. She spent days drilling into the foam with nail scissors to create air holes for Mark and making corresponding incisions on the pink fabric sleeve that would cover the foam. She sheared off lengths of organza and bunched them up before gluing them to the foam, to create rolls and lumps in the intestines.

Once she finished sewing the sleeve from the pink fabric, Mark came over to help her cover the foam.

'This reminds me of my invalid grandmother,' he said, gathering it all up in his arms and turning it inside out. 'I had to roll on her stockings sometimes. Don't sneer. I was a doting grandson.'

When Ingrid continued to sneer, he dropped the sleeve over her head so she was consumed.

'Oh no. Help,' she said.

It took them both a long time to pull the sleeve along the whole length of the foam. It struggled over the mounds of organza, and she still had to sew up one end and fashion a pillowcase-like fold on the other end to obscure the opening for Mark.

'Shall I test it now?' he asked.

'But what if you don't fit?'

'You measured my widest part.'

'Yes, but it could have gone wrong.'

Mark did not have time to climb inside before the producer arrived. The three of them fed the intestines into the back of the van and were only just able to shut the doors. They needed Mark for rehearsals, so he said goodbye to Ingrid, leaving her with two tickets for the following week's first performance.

Once he was gone, she tided the workshop, putting the remains of the fabric in the scraps drawer and hoovering up foam scales. She started to close, but as she was turning off the lights, she found Sir over in Mr Guratsky's station. He was in two halves, as if the puppeteer had opened his hand—Sir's mouth—too wide. The tear in the fabric started at the edges of Sir's mouth and went all the way to the back of his throat.

*   *   *

The Lois was all on one level; there was no incline as you neared the stage. It was more like a school hall. In the corner was a table with collapsible legs holding an array of juices and wine.

From the ceiling Ingrid could hear something churning, like a giant, hard-working machine. She followed the sound with her eyes, where it ended above the stage. Even as the theatre began to fill, the bowling alley could still be heard over the audience's conversations.

Ingrid was in the third row from the back, in a classroom chair with legs that could be joined together with all the other chairs in the row. The seat beside her, the closest to the aisle, was for Mr Guratsky, but he would not be joining her.

'I love your bag,' the woman next to her said.

'Thank you. It's made from the same material as one of the props,' Ingrid said.

'Oh.'

The woman turned away.

As she waited for the performance to begin, Ingrid pinched a cut on her finger. It had been a difficult task to fix Sir for the final time; she was not used to sewing something so small after weeks with the intestines. Sir was retiring. The studio had decided he wouldn't film any more bumpers. They were making merchandise out of the other fish, who were all much more uniform with their plastic mouths. They had discovered, in their market research, that not many children understood what Sir was. One child they surveyed thought he was a talking rock.

Ingrid reached into her bag. Sir was inside. Mr Guratsky had allowed her to keep him. It was only after she'd fixed his gaping mouth that the studio had made their decision to go on without him. She reached her hand into his body and gently opened and closed his mouth. He was still talking when the play began.

It was set in a laboratory. There were unnaturally tall flasks and test tubes and six men in white coats. Mark played a friendly technician whom no one seemed to like. He spoke an odd, made-up language that only one of the other scientists could understand. The audience laughed whenever he spoke. He wore thick glasses and rushed around the stage constantly. Ingrid had to shift in her seat to keep sight of him.

There was something important happening in the lab. Everyone was under pressure and Mark's character was often in the way. In a fit of rage, when Mark made a vital mistake and tarnished the research, another scientist killed him.

When he came back to life, he was even more manic than before. Ingrid switched to Mr Guratsky's seat so she could see Mark more clearly.

'Don't worry. I know what's happened,' the one scientist translated over and over, despite Mark's line changing drastically every time. The other men, terrified, would not let him near their research.

The scientists changed focus. Instead of their important work, they all theorised and experimented with different ways to kill Mark, but nothing, not decapitation nor dismemberment, would work. No one could see Mark anymore. He was obscured behind a desk and his deaths conveyed through the blood on the scientists' lab coats.

Throughout his deaths, Mark kept speaking.

'I know what's happened,' the translator continued.

Finally, one scientist suggested they set him on fire. To represent this, they drew the curtains and played sound effects of a liquid being poured, then a lighter. The few lights above the stage went red and all the men screamed, then all the lights went out. People in black began to run through the audience carrying the intestines. A section was draped on Ingrid's lap. She held it closely to her.

When the lights returned, dimly, the lab was empty, except for the end of the intestines. The rest travelled through the audience, over their feet or over their heads. A woman across the aisle from Ingrid pushed it off her shoulder, which meant it hugged her waist instead.

Someone at the other end of Ingrid's row squealed.

'It's moving,' they said.

The movement was faint, but there was a shift that did not seem to be caused by anyone else.

Ingrid waited patiently, until she felt a weight on her lap. Where others flinched and squirmed when they had felt Mark's form inside, she rested her elbows on the foam and whispered an imitation of Mark's strange language into the air hole.

Others in the audience continued to scream, and some laughed to cope. The lights roamed around the room, which tricked people. It could make it seem as if the intestines were pulsing or rolling forward, but Mark was still on top of Ingrid.

There was a particularly large commotion in the front row. People either shrank away or leaned in for a closer look when they felt the intestines moving, which, in turn, created more movements.

Ingrid looked at the air hole. It was too dark to see inside. She began to slide her fingers inside to test the strength of the foam, whether it could take her whole hand and allow her to find Mark's inside.

The front row was louder now. Someone stood up and pointed to the set of three stairs leading to the shallow stage.

Ingrid's hand burst into the cavity. She reached further in.

There was applause. Ingrid looked up. Mark was standing on the stage, beside the end of the intestines. He was bowing.

Everyone was standing now. The scientists reconvened on the stage to bow. Ingrid yanked her hand free and stood as well. Her claps did not seem to make a sound, did not seem to add anything to the applause. She leaned into the aisle and tried to catch Mark's eye. He didn't seem to notice.

MUSTAPHA ENESI

One Good Thing

Mrs Silifa is pregnant again.

Every day, as she has for the last forty years, she wakes up with an enormous mass of anger in her throat. It is engorged, heavy with the past she has sworn never to let go, and pumping fuel into her hatred for Bisi with each day it remains.

She was twenty-one years old when she took her first pregnancy test. Exactly four weeks before taking the test, she'd skipped school with Bisi, her best friend at the time, to attend an all-night party at Bar Beach. She ended up, after a couple of drinks, with some guy—or a couple of guys, she never recalled. All she remembered was how she'd woken up sore and horrified. And though Bisi thought she had exaggerated because Mrs. Silifa was good at making small things seem big, she felt responsible for persuading her to go to the party.

Mrs. Silifa had crouched over a bowl in Bisi's bathroom, the same way she now crouches over a potty in her boyfriend's bathroom, a test strip in her hands, doubting the signs she had been noticing. She should not be pregnant at sixty-two years old. Not after five children, a cheating husband who had died of stroke, and menopause.

She stands up, slides the test strip into the potty, walks into the room and sees Ben eating what's leftover of the beans she made the night before. The smell upsets her—she thinks about all the years she potty trained her children, the dreadful nature of motherhood, the little moments of happiness she captured in her children's laughter, the stench of diapers, the pain in their cries, and the sleepless nights; years she gave her life away, while her husband turned his penis into a community commodity; the sacredness of their marriage laid bare, stained by the impurities of Okene girls, like ink stains on white clothes—and she rushes back to the bathroom. Ben hears the sound of vomiting and running water. He pauses for a minute and thinks about rushing to the bathroom, too. But the sound is gone just as soon as it has started and he goes back to eating.

When Mrs Silifa returns to the room, she looks clean, her heavily contoured face hiding her worry and skin folds and wrinkles. Ben is done eating and is punching the keypads of the PlayStation she got for him on his twenty-fourth birthday two years ago. She walks to him and plants a kiss on his forehead. Bean residue hangs on his goatee and his breath smells of spoiled food. It doesn't upset her this time. She adjusts her head-tie and searches for her shoes around the room.

"So, what does the test say?"

"Go and brush your mouth, Ben. The beans you ate was bad."

"Is it positive? Are you pregnant?" Ben asks with so much enthusiasm.

"The weather is so humid, food is spoiling fast."

"So, we are not having a baby?"

"Bring the rest of the beans to the Staff Quarters tonight. We can feed it to Charlie. And I will make goat meat pepper soup for you." Mrs. Silifa says.

She walks to the door and turns the knob to leave when Ben asks, "Why are you avoiding my questions?"

She stops, sighs, looks back at Ben and says, "I'm late for work, Ben. We will talk later."

*   *   *

Later, when she gets to her office, Simbi, her cleaner, has everywhere looking sharp.

Pens in the pen holder. Exam sheets at the corner of her vast desk. Administrative files here. Cooperative files there. More files. Everything took a space, leaving a small empty rectangle where she places her laptop. Simbi used to work at the University's canteen as a waiter. She would take orders from lecturers and students and students' relatives who had come to visit, and she would smile at them. She has the most beautiful smile. Her smiles were forced sometimes and other times they were genuine. On some days, her genuine smiles displaced the forced ones after a generous tip from one of the many ludicrous male lecturers who all wanted something more than the gift of her smiles. When Mrs. Silifa finally met her, Simbi had warmed up to her. At first, because Mrs. Silifa was the kindest person she had met at the University. She didn't laugh at her spoken English the way others did or ask about her age because she looked young; and how could a woman her age be uneducated in a university environment. She was simply kind and warm and accessible. And on top of that, she tipped her nicely. When Simbi found out that not only did Mrs. Silifa grew up in the same town she was from, but she also spoke and understood Ebira perfectly, even more than she did, she hugged her tightly. Mrs. Silifa offered her a cleaning job—a receptionist, she had told the school because she was due for one. Simbi accepted.

"What is happening in school today Simbi? Tell me what I don't know," Mrs. Silifa says as she sits on her chair.

"I hear say cooperative wan strike. Na wetin everybody dey talk."

"Again? Well, that is something interesting."

Simbi's English should have been better by now. But Mrs. Silifa stopped paying for her classes for reasons best known to her. Even though Simbi believed it was because she was smarter and perhaps Mrs. Silifa was scared she would steal her job, she didn't complain.

"Sit down Simbi." Mrs. Silifa gestures towards one of the chairs facing her and Simbi hesitates. The last time she was that free around her—not knocking before entering her office, sitting down before being offered a seat, eating Mrs. Silifa's leftover food or food she suddenly did not have an appetite for, gossiping—she had walked in on her making out with Ben. It was around that time Mrs. Silifa stopped paying for her classes and she never asked why.

"How old are you now Simbi?"

"25, Mah."

"Do you have a man?"

Simbi blushes a little, "Yes, Mah."

"Does he work in this University?"

"Yes, Mah, is Mr. Ojo, Mah."

"The female hostel porter?" Mrs. Silifa is taken by surprise.

Simbi blushes some more. "He speaks English, very good, Mah."

Mrs. Silifa sighs, "Do you think he is going to marry you?"

"Yes Mah, as second wife, Mah."

"Will you have–" Mrs. Silifa does not finish her question when loud, raspy, singing voices cut in. They are singing 'Solidarity is forever' and for a moment, she wishes she could join them. To just remove her head tie, walk out of her office and join the Junior Staff in their peaceful protest against the government.

"You can go Simbi, I will call you when I need you."

Simbi hurries out, leaving the door open behind her. Mrs. Silifa moves to her door and closes it, feeling a little bit wholesome, a little bit bereft. She takes out her phone and thinks about calling all of her children, one after the other. Just to ask if they are good, if their husbands are treating them well, and maybe tell them that she may be pregnant. She doesn't.

*　*　*

Mrs. Silifa returns home before dinner time.

The school was just resuming after the eight-month strike and there was barely anything for her to do. Her first class is set to start the following week. And after spending all day ruminating over the past in her head, she needs a moment of calm. She needs Ben. She needs sex. She takes out her phone and flings her bag onto the black tuxedo sofa in the sitting room. Charlie rushes towards her and whimpers. She rubs her terrier's fur and walks past her. Mrs. Silifa's house is black and white, a picture of something from a 50's movie. Black sofas and curtains against white painted walls. She texts Ben:

Hey baby, could you stop by the mall on your way and get Durex lubricant? Peppersoup will be ready in a moment.

She heads to her room to change into a nightgown and Charlie follows her. She returns to the sitting room and slouches on the sofa, briefly, before heading into the kitchen. When she opens the deep freezer and brings the frozen goat meat out, her doorbell goes off. Ben is early. She abandons the meat and goes to open the door for him. They hug, they kiss. Ben withdraws from her and tosses a nylon bag to the sofa.

Ben spends most of his nights at Mrs. Silifa's apartment in the Staff Quarters. During the first week they started seeing, the sex was frequent. It was the best thing that had happened to Mrs. Silifa, five years after her husband's death. They had met at the university's restaurant when Simbi still worked as a waiter. It started as an act of kindness, generous Mrs. Silifa rescues young, broke and stranded Ben who couldn't afford to pay for lunch. Numbers were exchanged at first and in a couple of weeks, bodies were exchanged, too. In the vast two-bedroom apartment Mrs. Silifa owned, the heat of the sex consumed them both. In her office, at the staff bathroom, in the discomfort of Ben's mini apartment, they fucked everywhere, nonstop, for seven days.

"Did you see my text?" He asks.

"What text?" Mrs. Silifa wipes her lips with the back of her hand. She feels giddy.

"Eniola is coming to Lagos."

"Eniola? Who is Eniola?"

"My cousin, remember? The one that went to London School of Economics, the banker?"

"Oh, that one," Mrs. Silifa is uninterested.

"She will be staying at my place for some time. There was a flood and it didn't look good from what she told me."

"How long is she staying?"

"I don't know, she really needs my help. Besides, your place is better than mine anyway. Isn't that what you always wanted? To always meet at yours, yes?" Ben moves closer to Mrs. Silifa and grabs her buttocks.

She stirs away, "I have to finish the soup, the meat should have defrosted by now," she says, and leaves for the kitchen.

"I got the lube," Ben says in excitement, following her, "it is a bit expensive, and my last betnaija game did not–"

"I will wire you some money in the morning," Mrs. Silifa cuts in.

"What about this morning? Are you ready to talk about it?"

Mrs. Silifa does not reply. She turns on the tap and begins to rinse the meat under running water. "Grab me a bowl from the shelf, please."

Ben stifles a frown and hands her a blue bowl. "You really don't want to talk about it." Mrs. Silifa takes a quick glance at Ben, and the white noise of the running water breaks the silence that exists between them, the house and the question Ben had asked.

"You know, you remind me of my last born, Oyiza, stubborn child. She is the same age as you."

"There you go again! Waiting for the perfect moment to bring this up. It is always age this, age that."

Mrs. Silifa, shocked at the rage in Ben's voice, does not say a word, she turns on the gas and places the pot of goat meat on it. Ben moves closer to her and wraps his arms around her body. His breath caresses her neck. His chin, warm against her body. She reaches for salt. Maggi. Pepper. Curry. Thyme. Pepper soup spice.

"We are equals in this relationship. No age, no status," Ben whispers into her ear and kisses her on the neck.

"Equals?" Mrs Silifa frowns; she turns around. "Your house rent. Your clothes. Your phone. Your feeding allowance. School fees. Family bills. I pay for everything. We are not equals Ben. We will never be equals. The only thing you are good at is fucking!"

"Oh," Ben says. He turns back and walks away from Mrs. Silifa and she hears the main door slamming shut behind him. She scoops hot sauce from her boiling pot of goat meat to taste. There is too much salt. She goes to the sitting room and checks Ben's nylon. There is no beans. Just lube. She picks up her phone and texts him:

You forgot to bring the beans for Charlie.

She goes into the kitchen, turns off the gas. There are several ceramic plates and food flasks of different sizes in her cabinets. There are mugs. China plates. Wine glasses. Glass cups. Plastic plates. Plastic cups. Plastic spoons. A set of nonstick pots. Two sets of nonstick frying pans. Stainless plates. Stainless cups. Stainless spoons. Forks. A complete collection of kitchen utensils enough to serve four houses sits in her kitchen. They remind her of another life. Five years ago, they sat in her husband's house, somewhere in Okene. They were mostly wedding gifts from friends and family. And in a weird way, they had always been there. They had become emblems of her transition into womanhood, and had followed her to her matrimonial home and everywhere she had moved to after. The night they started coming in from familial hands was the night she decorated her hands with henna. It was her wedding eve. She was so in love that she had begged the henna lady to write the name of her husband-to-be on the small of her back. The lady refused; she had too many hands to design, there wasn't enough time to glorify a man's ego. Men are not worth it she had told her. She laughs as she remembers the henna lady at her wedding. She laughs at the honesty of her words. She cleans the kitchen, dishes out the goat meat for Charlie, and goes to bed.

* * *

The next morning Mrs. Silifa listens to Simbi talk about the cooperative's looming strike.

"This thing dey serious o. I hear say the strike go begin tomorrow and dem go block road."

"Well, that is not a bad thing is it? Oppression should not be tolerated," Mrs. Silifa says.

Simbi nods, and starts to finish up her cleaning; she only needs to wipe the window louvres and she will be done. She hums as she cleans, a smile plastered on her face. A woman like Simbi— new to life, untouched by the many dangers of it—would find happiness in the most mundane things, like dating a man as old as her father. A lost woman she is, but no doubt, happily lost. She will be protected by frivolities, her youth, and maybe, good sex. Perhaps, it is the sex, Mrs. Silifa thinks. Her own sex life was never as exciting as it is now. Twenty years of married life, five daughters, and not once did she experience the beauty of orgasms, not until Ben. Maybe, it is different for Simbi, and all she can think about is how lucky Simbi is. Maybe she's found some luck as well, this pregnancy may just be a reward, one good thing that will change the small number of years she has left. A son, perhaps. A beautiful boy.

"How is your lover, Simbi?"

Simbi giggles, and says, "He is well Mah, I see am for night yesterday."

"He takes good care of you, doesn't he?"

"Yes, Mah, he buy me many things."

"That is good. Love is a good thing, isn't it?."

Simbi nods yes.

"Everyone deserves love. Or at least something that makes them happy. Some people go searching for that one good thing and they never find it. And soon they come to a realisation that their lives may be meaningless, that they may never be happy, so they stop searching."

Simbi smiles in agreement.

"Some stubborn people never stop searching. They search for it in other people's happiness: their partner's wealth, their children's successes elevates their spirits. They live through extensions of themselves. Some never find it at all, no matter how stubborn they are. A few find it in old age. When they have weak bones, old organs, and their lives are zooming closer to an end. That is when they find a meaning. But really, what is the purpose of life? There is no purpose to life, is there?"

Simbi shakes her head.

"You do understand what I am saying, don't you? That one must learn to live, to take life as it comes."

"Yes, yes, Mah, I understand Mah."

Simbi finishes her cleaning and leaves. Mrs. Silifa takes out her phone—there are no texts from Ben. His Instagram story has pictures of him and Eniola smiling into the screen. She wishes she could talk to her girls like she used to. Her relationship with Simbi is something she wishes she had with her daughters. The last time they were close, all five of them hugging her in unison, was during her husband's burial. It was one of the few times she felt like a mother. It was also the last time she had seen them. The other time she felt like a mother was when she had gone searching through her husband's phone, looking at texts messages and emails and strange phone numbers and WhatsApp texts from strange names. Searching for a sign that her husband was cheating. Some evidence. And when she did find something—a lot of things—her daughters comforted her. But her girls are all grown up now, tolerating the throes of marital life, motherhood, and occupation. And maybe, they are still new to life, untouched by the many dangers of it, finding happiness in the most mundane things. Maybe they are happily lost women. Maybe they are having great sex.

Mrs. Silifa stands by the window in her office and watches the Junior Staff brandishing placards with their messages in big block letters: **PAY US! GIVE US OUR RIGHT! TREAT US WELL! NA BETA WE WANT.** They are ululating and flailing arms and stamping feet and shouting and singing; *'We no go gree o. We no go gree.'* After watching for a while, she picks up her bag and leaves for Ben's house.

*   *   *

Ben's house looks clean when Mrs. Silifa gets there.

The usual masculine stench that hangs heavy around his place is gone, replaced by a sweet orangey smell. The plates are clean. The floors are shiny. The laundry basket is empty. And she is surprised. Has he improved? Is he trying to become better because of what she said the night before? Perhaps it is Eniola who has cleaned everywhere. Mrs. Silifa feels the pangs of jealousy clawing her neck. She was sorry to have said what she had said. But she isn't going to admit it or apologise for that matter. That will make her look weak. And God Forbid, it will make them seem equal. For Mrs. Silifa, when a man thinks he is better than you, that is when he begins to exert control, subtly at first, and before one knows it, you are asking them to permit you to drink a glass of water. Or telling them that your male colleague is just your male colleague and nothing else. A man's insecurity is a feeble thing. It snaps faster than a dry twig.

Eniola struts out of the tiny kitchen in the apartment—a table spoon in her hand, her hair packed in a hair bonnet—to meet Mrs. Silifa standing under the ceiling fan. Ben walks out of the bathroom immediately after. Eniola's body is drenched in sweat and a pink linen vest clings to her chest and she looks like she is in her mid-thirties. Mrs. Silifa can tell that Eniola is not wearing a bra, too, and that she is tired. The tiny kitchen, giving room for little air to pass through it, explains her sweating but nothing explains Ben's sweating. Despite the fact that he is in shorts and is brandishing his bare, chiselled chest all over the apartment.

"Welcome Madam. Welcome Ma," Eniola says.

"Enhen. Thank you. I heard about the flood? How is your husband?"

"He is fine. We thank God that he was not at home when the flood started. He went to Brazil and last week he was in Rwanda. He will be travelling to Sweden next month, you know, work work work. And me?" Eniola pauses to chuckle, "I went to the village to visit my mother o. I bought her provisions from Shoprite. If you see how she was dancing and praising me eh."

Mrs. Silifa decides she doesn't like Eniola. "So you are not working? Why are you not working?" she asks, and without waiting for Eniola to respond, says, "Why do you want to useless your London degree?"

"I will work. I am going to work. But you see, my husband and I think it is better we have the kids first before I start."

Ben is unusually quiet, on his bed, fanning himself with a cover of an exercise book. Normally, he would have chipped in and talked about feminism and equality and the subtle internalised misogyny women suffered from. But he just keeps fanning himself.

"You and your husband think that is what is best? Or your husband thinks it is the best?" Mrs. Silifa asks.

Eniola feels uneasy and chooses not to answer.

"Ben tells me a lot about you. Your kindness is immeasurable, God will bless you and bless all the students you have guided at the University," she says instead, a wide smile on her face.

"Guided? Is that what Ben tells you? That I am guiding him?"

Eniola does not reply. Ben scratches his afro.

"En- Eniola made fish stew. Sh-should I bring some?" Ben struggles to say. He always loses his calmness when he is hiding something. He stands up and walks to the kitchen and he brushes shoulders with Eniola and he shifts and she shifts. And Mrs. Silifa gasps.

"Jesus, Ben! You are fucking your married cousin."

She is shocked at first, at her discovery but then she realises that she is more unsure of what to feel about what she said. Would it have been okay if Eniola wasn't married?

*   *   *

Mrs. Silifa rushes to her house later in the evening.

She is having a fever and her stomach is cramping with unbearable pain. She turns and squirms on the sofa. She unties her head tie and flings it. She pushes out her shoes. Her bag lies at the other end of her house. Charlie runs towards her and barks a little; she shoos her away and rolls to the floor. She doesn't remember the last time she had cramps. It seems like ages ago even though her menopause started seven years ago. And after all these years, one would think she would have overcome the pain of cramps. She feels her stomach turn and twist and eventually streams of blood begin to flow down her legs.

She lets out a scream. Charlie goes back to her, whimpering and licking her face. And Mrs. Silifa, on her black carpeted floor, curls into a human ball and cries.

By the time she stands up, it is almost midnight. She goes to her fridge and takes out a bottle of vodka. She takes large gulps. Her eyes are red. Her face is swollen. She looks for her bag and, when she finds it, searches for her phone in a frenzy. There are many missed calls and text messages from Ben. She doesn't open them. Instead, she goes to WhatsApp and video calls all of her daughters. All five of them. Oyiza's face is the first to appear on the screen. Her eyes are bright. Her chin, smooth. Her goggles are neat and behind her there is a Christmas tree and children playing and laughing. This makes Mrs. Silifa happy.

"Hello mom, long time. And very strange that you are calling."

"How is America? Is it treating you well?" Mrs. Silifa asks.

"You don't look good Mommy, everything alright?"

"I want to tell you girls something, let's wait for your sisters, okay?"

"We both know they won't pick your call. What is it Mama? Do you need money?"

"I-I am trying-"

"Just send a text and I'll wire you the money tomorrow. I need to go."

Mrs. Silifa hears Oyiza shouting at the kids before the phone goes off.

*

The next day, she rushes down to school in tight black spaghetti trousers and boots. Her hair is packed in a hair net, and she is wearing a blue gym vest that makes her underarms jiggle. She joins a mob of lecturers and Junior Staff at the roadblock by the entrance of the university's gate. Her placard reads: **DO NOT FUCK WITH OUR FUTURE.** Somehow, for as long as she lives, there is a future she looks forward to. And somehow, she is hopeful that she will find that one good thing, no matter how long it takes.

ASIA HAUT

Margot

She will always be grateful for the name they gave her. On that first afternoon, when she walked into the Writer's Room and Peter revealed she was to be called Margot, she found herself thinking everything had the potential to be okay. It had just stopped raining and the sun had come out in that crazy way it sometimes does following a downpour, all abrupt and gleamy. For a moment, every face in the room was illuminated and each one of them was beautiful, even Peter with his appalling posture and tendency to blink too much. Straight away she thought the name conveyed a cool-headedness, or a cold-bloodedness, she wasn't sure she knew the difference. Either way, Margot wasn't the type that was easily intimidated, not someone who worried about money, struggled with small talk, or feared getting old. The name in no way resembled her own, they didn't share a single letter in common. Margot would never allow a man to shove her against a wall and call her stuff.

The entire writing team had gathered round her, and by way of a response she did the thing that made her look like she was lost in thought – it had been a key mannerism for a character that had earned her two nominations, though no actual awards. Having completed the gesture, which always took longer than she remembered, she tilted her face towards Michael and Peter and declared the name *perfect*. They were the head writers and co-showrunners and basically called the shots. Peter's eyelashes fluttered like butterfly wings and Michael scratched at his straggly beard and grinned at her in an avuncular fashion. Only the previous year, Michael had kissed her on a narrow balcony in Northern France; now it was all benevolent smiles. The writers continued to stare and she supposed they wanted more. So, standing in the last remaining patch of sunlight, she conjured up another look from her repertoire, then said the name slowly as if trying it on for size. Two syllables, the second forcing her lips forward in a manner she hadn't anticipated. Then her cheeks flushed furiously because, for once, none of it was acting.

* * *

That introduction had taken place more than six years ago, meaning that the period in which she *was* Margot extends behind her like a bridal train. She had thought she was walking towards something, turns out everything was always in her wake. And these days she finds it hard to imagine how she ever had the guts to become an actress, how she had not disintegrated in the face of all that scrutiny and brutal rejection. When she recalls stepping on stage for the very first time, a fifteen-year-old who had no idea what acting was, auditioning against girls five and six years her senior, she worries that it has the whiff of a lazy backstory. The memory is too like something an inexperienced script editor would come up with to flesh out a role, a way of establishing that a character has always had chutzpah. She has never had chutzpah, or guts, or anything along those lines.

*   *   *

When she was a girl of nine or ten years old, her father, a large man with exacting standards, went through a phase of taking her on long drives. The purpose of these trips wasn't to end up anywhere – they were never heading towards a picnic-spot or zoo – but simply to maintain a forward trajectory. Her father used the time they spent together as an opportunity to talk about *things*, to speak to her as though she were an adult, to ask her opinion. Unfortunately, she was the sort of daughter who was unwilling to voice an opinion, and her father would become angry, and the day would be ruined. But offering up her interior life for inspection was too painful, especially when she wasn't fully convinced that she possessed one. So, these excursions always went the same way: his disquisition, their aborted exchange, the terrible silence that ensued. Her reticence met with his wordless rebuke. Only once can she remember him interrupting the punishing silence.

'I sometimes wonder if all this *having nothing to say for yourself* is your way of criticising me. To someone who values communication, it does feel rather pointed. Or maybe you really do have nothing to contribute.'

As he continued theorising, the car drove past a field full of goldenrod, and before it had even disappeared from view, she was missing it terribly, wondering what it would feel like to submerge herself in the rippling yellow. She glanced at her father still dissecting her character, then let her eyes rest on the rear-view mirror. Only road behind them. Too soon, the bright field had receded into memory.

No, the decision to act never had anything to do with guts, but stemmed instead from the realisation that a lifetime spent being solely herself would be unbearable. She might as well slit her wrists. Instead, she took up acting. From the start she was regarded as talented. While still at drama school, a tutor, the one who regularly reduced them all to tears, praised her for playing the part of Cordelia with a *masochistic honesty*.

'This quality,' he said, lolling on a sofa so horribly orange she thought she would swoon, 'will be the making of you.'

If she had been a different sort of person, she might have asked how it was he couldn't see that her *honesty* was merely a means of concealing a more humiliating truth. But she was who she was and therefore didn't. She, by contrast, has always reckoned that any talent she has lies in her face. Not that she considers it anything special, especially not now that the years are catching up with her, but because it communicates an emptiness begging to be filled. All she needs is a writer. A half-decent script.

*   *   *

Margot is loved. Not universally, but more than enough. It is no exaggeration to say that a tremendous number of people love her. She certainly does. She loves Margot in ways she is unable to articulate. When Peter and Michael provided her with character notes, she had always accepted them unquestioningly, quietly taken on board all of their ideas. Michael calls her *porous*. Though this sounds unpleasant, like there might be something wrong with her skin, it's meant as a compliment, is his way of saying that she instinctively soaks up direction, then exudes what was requested, word for word. According to certain critics, long-form television is this era's dominant artform, meaning that for the last five series she has been not only *porous*, but something of intrinsic worth. But everything has an end point, which is where she currently finds herself. The finale was released on streaming platforms a fortnight ago, and now she is reeling like someone recently bereaved, stumbling like a drunk person in the direction of a bathroom that's not been cleaned in weeks. She peers in a mirror flecked with toothpaste; the tiny white spit-globs like faraway stars.

'Nothing,' she enunciates to no one, because, at this precise moment, no one is waiting for her to speak.

Back in the bedroom she picks up the laptop that she earlier left discarded on a sea of crumpled sheets and jabs at the button in the upper right-hand corner. She types out her name. *About 7,200,000 results (0.53 seconds)* it helpfully tells her at the top of the screen. How can there be so fucking much of her? When did this multiplication and dissemination take place? She pictures a dandelion clock slowly being blown, a tumour metastasizing. Next, she types out Margot's full name, including the various aliases. *About 10,800,000 results (0.57 seconds).* More, much more, though a fraction slower. Everything is there, laid out for her immediate consumption. She could crawl back into bed and gorge herself for hours. But today she doesn't want to read what everyone is saying about Margot, she has no desire to know how the ending was *breathtaking, the biggest pile of shit* they had ever seen. This morning she doesn't wish to learn that Margot was *the most nuanced character in a generation, the Maggot that ruined it for everyone – dumb bitch should have had her throat slit in series one.* Never again will she get to inhabit Margot's body, from this point on Margot belongs to everybody else. She gnaws at a ragged bit of skin at the root of her fingernail. Clicks open a video.

*   *   *

When Michael sat beside her on the plane, she wondered if he even remembered kissing her that time in France, or if all the film festival wine had erased it from his memory. It wasn't like it had been a good kiss, in fact she had categorised it as bad, and decided to put it out of her mind as he had apparently done. Yet details had stuck – like how the balcony railings were all ornate and swirling and there had been nowhere for her to rest her glass of wine, how he'd nearly trodden on her toe and his apology had made her laugh, how the feel of his beard against her skin had made her worry she might sneeze. But the minute he stretched out his legs – ample leg-room, even for him, in First Class – and suggested they get drinks, she knew that the next eight hours or so would be spent flirting on and off. Up in the air it was all performance, a way for both of them to say that even though he wrote so well for her, even though he instinctively understood what would sound perfect coming out of her mouth, he wasn't the slightest bit interested in her – it was all about Margot. Having reached altitude, she realised that she had assumed Margot's cadence, a rhythm that he and Peter had, of course, composed. She even quoted a line of his dialogue back at him; nothing dramatic or particularly suggestive, just something Margot had said to Lowell the night they met in that dingy basement bar in episode three of series two, which seemed to slot neatly into conversation. Michael acknowledged his work with the kind of smile that made her imagine she knew what he had looked like as a teenager – a smattering of acne across the forehead and slightly rounded shoulders because he wasn't yet comfortable with his height. Above the ocean she really wasn't herself and, as a result, wanted him a great deal.

For the duration of the press junket, they spent all their nights together, not giving a second thought to the recklessness of their behaviour. Peter and the actors were forced to pretend that they hadn't noticed what was going on.

Her favourite part of each day was when all the boring interviews were at last over, and it was just the two of them getting ready before they went out for food. Moving slowly around the hotel room – 'Have you seen my top? My other shoe?' – she would feel his eyes tracking her like a camera, as dying light filtered through a window looking out across a city that neither of them fully knew. On the fifth night, having got back from some place downtown that did the best dim sum he had ever eaten, they brushed their teeth standing side-by-side in front of the *His and Her* sinks. In the backlit mirror, they had looked like husband and wife. Her heart beat hard when he caught her gawking, and she had been sure he was about to say something that would change everything, but instead he dipped his head, glugged water straight from the tap, and swirled it round his mouth.

'You know,' he said, having spat it out, 'Margot is the best thing I've ever written. The best fucking thing.'

It was over the moment they checked out of the hotel. On the return flight they didn't even sit together, though at least that meant she got a window seat. When she made her way down the aisle, and passed Michael sat beside the actor who played Lowell – strange to think that both men had done things to her naked body – he'd glanced up at her and nodded. Locked inside the chemical-smelling toilet, she ran cold water over the insides of her wrists and tried to avoid catching her reflection in the mirror above the sink. But the cubicle was so small that escaping her face simply wasn't possible.

After a couple of hours, Peter took pity on her sat all alone, and the two of them had watched some dismal film together, shared a bowl of pistachio nuts, that left a weird greenish dust on the tips of her fingers. As soon as the credits started to roll, Peter cleared his throat.

'You know everything has a finite span,' he said, trying so hard to sound kind that he'd ended up blinking even more than usual.

It was a pathetic observation, for which she had been immensely grateful.

When they got off the plane, Michael's wife was there to meet him. She was called Abigail, had shoulder-length hair the colour of wet sand, and was a real person with real feelings.

The video she's clicked on is a scene from the penultimate episode of the final ever series. While she would never admit it to either Michael or Peter, she prefers this episode to the finale. Although it's quieter, far less dramatic, during the course of the hour a muffled tension escalates until it becomes too great to contain. Unlike the rest of the episode, this scene was shot in black and white. When she first discovered it wouldn't be in colour, she had worried that viewers would find it jarring or, worse still, pretentious. But Pavel, the Director of Photography, handles light and shadows like emotions, and the scene ended up feeling as though it could only ever have been in monochrome. Margot is sat alone on a train, leaving behind everything that she once loved. For such a long time, regret has been coiled inside her, but now, sat in a carriage surrounded by strangers, everything comes undone. A strangulated noise forces its way from her throat, but when she tries to suck it back in, her shoulders shake, then her whole body, and she is left hyperventilating. People leading normal lives turn around to look at her. She clutches at her stomach, then doubles forward as if in physical pain. Not a single person asks if she is okay. The crying becomes louder and, for a second, her whole face twists out of shape. Then the unsayable escapes. Too late, she slams a hand across her mouth, stunned by her own admission. Gradually the crying subsides until, once more, she is silent. She doesn't brush the tears away. They are hard-won diamonds on her cheeks. When the train reaches the next station, she gets off and is immediately lost in the crowd milling about on the platform.

This same scene again and again.

Margot, herself, someone else on continuous loop.

*　　*　　*

The thing that television and memories have in common is that both can be reshot.

*　　*　　*

Once more she is in the car with her father. This time his silence is not the worst thing in the world and her wordlessness is not shameful. Their quiet is companionable, is simply what the day is made out of. Perhaps they are on a road trip. She watches him staring ahead, his face in profile. The warm air makes her want to wriggle her toes; she is a child after all.

And then, as though out of nowhere, though she always knew it would come into view right about now, the field full of goldenrod. Rippling in the late-summer breeze, the tall yellow flowers make her heart thump so hard that she is sure her father must be able to hear the tremendous noise that she is currently making. But he is a polite man who would never dream of embarrassing his daughter by passing comment.

'Stop,' she says in a voice that is neither loud nor quiet, but perfectly modulated.

'Sorry, what did you say?'

'Please Daddy, can you stop the car.'

He does as she asks and pulls up by the side of the field. She unfastens her seatbelt, opens the door, and climbs out. His expression suggests a bemused indulgence. Having scrambled over a low fence, scarcely a fence at all, she enters the field and starts to run. Not in the normal way, like she does with friends on the school playground, but with her arms spread out either side of her body, as if she is suddenly much younger than she actually is and believes she is a bird about to take flight. It's nearing the end of the day and the sun is lying low in the sky. As she races, lickety-split, across the field, everything is golden. The light, the flowers, she herself. Specks of pollen stick to her skin, causing her arms and face to glisten. Though her father is a tall man, well over six foot, he has to crane his neck, so high are the flowers, so fast is she running. Standing at the brink of the field, he laughs softly to himself and shakes his head. This is the most vivid thing he has ever seen. It is like a closing scene. He will remember it forever.

'Margot sweetheart!' he calls out.

But the child does not turn around and continues running further and further away. It is as if she cannot hear him, has ceased to recognise the name, or is simply waiting for someone to shout *Cut*.

FRED LUNZER

In Canada, we trained our dogs to smell fire

When they asked me to take the place of Petr, I could have said no, but my first thought was that this would cause problems for my father, who was in debt to the Vanes and buying alcohol again. My mother gasped at the request, almost laughed at it, but then said nothing. Before I left, my bag ready and sitting beneath the pressed peonies in my bedroom, she came and sat next to me on my bed and placed a small black dagger on the quilt between us. The men would be no trouble, they wouldn't rape me, she said. Just like that. But better to be safe blah blah, and she gave a speech about how small the town now was, all the men dead in war or dead in drink or dead in spirit, and how we had a duty. And maybe it was good we did. She smiled. But she waited for me to take the dagger and put it into my bag.

In the end, the knife wouldn't be used for the jobs she'd dreamt up, slicing at thick hands, sliding into a Vane gut. But I used it for other jobs – the horses' bridle knots, some cooking, some surgery on the dogs when their paws picked up the gorse. The gorse encouraged the fires, so the fact that it also injured the dogs annoyed us all. I'd been permitted to take Ada with us, and I worried for her paws.

We left when the mornings were still cool, eight of us with four dogs and ten horses, moving in no particular formation towards the Handhills and the forests beyond.

On the way out of town, we passed a line of Preachers dressed in black, and they had a small conversation with Tom Vane, the eldest son. I didn't mind the Vanes, I thought much of what they did was logical. I didn't mind the Preachers either, I liked their seclusion and their independence, even if their religion was laughable. One of their women looked up at me, and we locked eyes, and I saw her surprise that I was joining for the sprawl. Or was it disapproval? Or was it envy? On the ground, I would have looked away, but sitting up on my horse I felt superior, like I was useful. On my other side, Ada sat watching me, her coat black like the Preachers' clothes, but silk to their wool.

If I felt fear then, I tried not to show it to the men. Jan Vane was a year younger than me and also on his first sprawl, and I thought I looked braver than him. The sprawl was strange in that many of us had never seen it, we

100

had just seen its results, like it was a disease we knew from its symptoms. For instance: smoke clouds in the far sky, ash flurries that turned our roofs white, burns on men who returned, head-shakes for men who didn't, lost dogs, lost horses, tears and drunkenness, nightmares howled across the houses at night… Less directly, we felt the stretch of the years when the Vanes' timber yard stood nearly empty, when money and supplies seemed to drain from the town.

So though I hadn't seen it myself, I felt I knew the sprawl. In the end I found that it had been named well: a rolling burn across the forests, a lazy grabbing of trees by fire.

*   *   *

We travelled for two days. The huts sat on the other side of the Handhills, not quite on the flat itself but close to it. The hills were the only elevation in that flat flat land, and the huts – they were barely shacks – sat on a kind of vantage point, a shelf of grass that the Vanes referred to as the settle. The weather was cold at the beginning, and on our first morning I looked out from the settle across the woods, shivering and not believing fire would ever be possible.

There were three days of rain, that's how unlikely fire felt. We were five Vanes, two Dieps and me, and it seemed I was the only one who felt wrong to sit inside the huts while the dogs were left outside. They were trained hard, and even before the prospect of fire, they sat out in front of the huts, watching and smelling the air for smoke. Even in the night, in the rain, they stayed there, sitting upright while their hair blew horizontal.

Ada had been trained too, by my father, but I couldn't stand it and on the rain's second day I made a quiet request to Tom Vane for her to stay by my cot, just through the bad weather. He looked disgusted, but he didn't say anything and I decided to take what I wanted from that. I was staying in the smaller hut with the young Jan Vane and the two Diep brothers, Sim and Isaac, and after it was dark I went crouching out into the downpour and carried Ada back in with me. Sim was by the fire and he looked at me but said nothing. Isaac and Jan were asleep, or pretending to be, and they must have woken anyway because Ada started barking at the fire and I had to jump on her and hold her mouth shut. I was horrified. She struggled, but eventually calmed, and I released her. She lay on her front and eyed the fire, which was just a simple stone pit, a chimney above it leading out through the ceiling. If you looked at the huts from the outside, you knew something was up, because the chimneys had

101

complicated hoods over them to catch any sparks. But Ada didn't understand this and she sat whining for a few minutes, her long black face pointing at the fire, until I gave her a small kick and threatened to throw her out into the rain. The next morning, I put her back outside before the older men were up for their jobs.

Sprawl workers have two jobs, preparing for fire and fighting fire, and we started on the first immediately. Preparing for fire is strangely like making fire. There were the pits we dug for water, and the clearing of gorse – as much as we could, and that was a bitter job – but there was also the controlled burning of dead undergrowth, and there was the stacking of firewood at different points on the land. The idea is that fire feeds on trees, so sometimes if a fire is racing down a wood, you want to set fire to a few trees in its path, so it has nowhere further to go.

'To stop fire, you start fire,' said Jakob Vane, the next one down from Tom.

You needed precision, and the wind on your side, but they said Jakob was an expert in it.

The Vanes knew the woods, knew the tree varieties, knew what was at risk, knew what was still young, knew what would be harvested in the fall and how. They carried bright red string with them and even now wrapped it around certain trunks, marking out the ones ready for felling. It seemed to me they knew everything about both the life of the trees and also their destruction – by fire or by felling – and I once remarked on this. It flattered Tom Vane's ego and he bragged about my comment to Jakob. They laughed, calling themselves the masters of life and death, but inside I smirked at the word 'masters'. To the north and east lay long tracts of vanished forest, where the sprawl had taken before and where the emptiness was creeping in.

* * *

We prepared for the fires and we practiced the dogs. Seven of us would stay at the huts while Jakob Vane slipped down into the forests. He took a sack of water, a blanket, muslin, a pocket watch, matches. At the closest quarter hour mark, he lit his small fire and we timed the dogs for their response. Those were pleasant minutes waiting at the huts, acting to the dogs like nothing was happening, watching the vast green with no idea where Jakob might be. The dogs were fast, and I was happy to see that Ada was often the first to prickle in her seat, raise her head, run to the edge of the settle and start barking. The four of them would then bark their way towards the fire, and we would ride after them to where Jakob had already doused it. The dogs would receive effusive praise, the kindest I ever saw the Vanes, and Tom Vane would dole out meat, the largest piece going to the first barker. Out of the ten tests we did, Ada won it six times.

Through this early period, I made friends with Jan Vane, but our friendship grew painful and I ended it. He was quiet, kind, and quick to help if I needed it. If he needed it, I helped him too. One day I took a gorse thorn the size of a finger out of his ankle. Another day I missed breakfast and he saved me some of his. One night Tom Vane was counting up the cutlery and saw that a spoon was missing. He got angry and made everyone account for their actions that day, and it was then that Jan realised he had left his spoon at lunch, down on the west fringe by the three-year-olds. Tom hauled him out of the hut and they rode right then in the dark, when there wasn't even any sun for the spoon to catch, all the way to the west fringe, and Tom made him search for the spoon until he found it. When Jan returned to our hut, his right eye was the size of an apple and there was blood in his pale fringe. His lip bled too. He said nothing, and readied his cot.

If it had only been that, I could have coped, but Jan kept making mistakes, and I kept having to roll over in my cot, face the wall and try not to see his new wounds. I stopped talking to him, everyone did, and it sickened me but I didn't have anything in me to give him.

More than anything, Tom Vane sickened me, I stopped thinking the Vanes were logical after that. It was evident to all of us that beating Jan had no positive effect on him or his mistakes, and in fact it seemed to be Jan's fear that motivated his clumsiness and forgetfulness. One afternoon I saw Ada lick his hand, and Jan flinched at first, pulled his hand back, but then he crouched and nuzzled against Ada's head. I thought that if all I could provide was my dog for comfort, at least that was something.

Partly I stopped speaking to Jan because I too was dreading a mistake. I had my own fears of making errors, my fears of forgetting things… my fears of Tom Vane and the older men, my fears of the sprawl. I think the others were just as scared, and at every opportunity we were checking our possessions, checking our tools. Sim and Isaac had some sort of list in their heads, and they patted up and down their bodies like a religious ritual. I became especially worried for the buttons on my jacket, and one day my fear was realised and I looked down and saw that one was missing.

This was horribly unfair, the weather was nearly warm enough not to need the jacket, and now one of its buttons was lying out there on the land, ready to catch the sun and twist it, bend it into fire. I spent a day in agony, fear galloping around my chest, terrified of what Tom would do if he found out, terrified a fire would start any second. I almost turned to Isaac and Sim for help, but that evening I was hanging up axes in our hut and a spin of light in the black wood wall caught my eye. The button had trapped between two planks, between two nubs of what once had been branches. I grabbed it and put it deep into my bag, almost weeping with relief, and that night I lay awake thinking about whether I had been incredibly fortunate or unfortunate. I stopped wearing my jacket and spent a week shivering through the mornings, but then the warmth came and I forgot all about it.

* * *

The first fire came easily enough one lunchtime, up in the north plot, exactly halfway across the land. The dogs called it and for a moment I wondered if the older Vanes had organised a test without telling us, tricking us like the dogs. But I saw Jakob was there beside us, and I saw the anguish in Tom Vane's face and knew it was real. It was true that the sun had been stronger, that the air was dryer; we felt it on the skin of our faces, in our puckered lips, our stretched eyes. And our hair had been oily in the mornings, our feet felt wider in our boots. When I walked out onto the settle each breakfast, I felt the pleasing temperature and dreaded its meaning.

We rode that first one down and Tom and Jakob threw us about it. The fear was high in my head, and I don't remember my actions well, during that fire or any of the following ones. We drew water from the pits, we pulled trees down, we blanketed and doused flames. The urgent thing was to stop the fire from rising up the trunks into the canopies – the trees held onto each other like friends drowning, and once the fire was in the canopies it would pass along the branches.

We handled that first fire, and returned at dusk to the huts. I sat on the settle and thought of the smoke, the heat, the pricks of fire on my face. I thought we had been lucky to succeed, because that day in the trees I had felt the dryness sucking, the air pleading for ignition. At one point I had felt something whump into my back and I thought a branch had fallen on me, but it was Jakob. An ember had caught my hair and he was smothering it. He shouted at me to tuck in my hair, and ran off. At the settle, I wanted to thank Jakob, but beyond our praise for the dogs – Ada had spotted that first one, I was proud – any meagre pleasantries or kindnesses fled that day.

Days later there was fire in the copse behind the settle, then one in the north plots again; and not long after that there was ground-smouldering

104

near the three-year-olds, near to where Jan had left his spoon that day. I was grateful he had found it then, his punishment would have been worse now. Tom Vane liked to do a kind of review of the fires, after we had put them out, no matter how late it was. He wanted to know how they had started, and it wasn't always clear, and that bothered him. He had two faces during that time, the one of anguish I had seen at the first fire, and the one of fury as he kicked through the wet mash of the dead fires, trying to find a cause. I thought he was looking for a solution, and I felt that smirk inside me again. I knew how to solve the sprawl, I had the answer: leave this place, don't come back, let it burn.

*   *   *

The settle transformed, it became more like a workshop or like the Vane's timber yard. Tom fussed about efficiency, he brought the horses onto the settle, along with their hitching rail and their feed, and he had us hang our tools neatly lined and with their owner marked, axe heads all pointing in the same direction. He nailed the hut doors open – we were to keep them that way, even through the night. We were to sleep clothed. We counted inventory constantly, and apart from our tools we no longer took metals down into the woods.

Tom Vane's second face, the furious one, appeared away from the fires too. At mealtimes – which were taken outside now, on the settle – conversation had turned sour and Tom would launch into monologues about our town, insulting different members of the community and what they did wrong. He was especially rude about my father, about his debt and his drinking, and sometimes he mentioned my mother. I felt that Tom hated her but didn't think he could insult a woman.

One dinner, he was pacing the settle and insulting his family's debtors, my father included, and he suddenly chucked his bowl down and stormed forward in my direction. In fact, I saw a cup in his hand, and saw that he was going to get water from the barrel behind me; but Isaac and Jan who were next to me didn't see the cup, and they jumped up and stood in front of me, blocking Tom's path. Tom veered off and walked slowly around them, looking confused and then shaking his head. He went to the barrel and asked their permission to take some water, mocking them. They sat back down again, and no one spoke.

I didn't know what to do with that, I had seen that both Isaac and Jan's hands were shaking. I felt foolish, like I had been oblivious to a danger, one that the other men saw clearly, and I cursed myself for my vanity, for thinking Tom hated my parents, when really he hated me.

Another day, two of the Preacher men came with a cart of hickory batons, which we were to use for the fires in our huts. Only the Preachers grew hickory, and the batons produced less smoke with a smell that wouldn't distract the dogs. I asked one of the Preachers for news from the town, and he asked me my family. When I told him, he said my father was sick, he had taken to his bed. I was shocked and for a moment felt sad, longing for home. But I couldn't be sure this wasn't simply his drinking – my father sometimes turned sprawl-like, drinking for days and days with an unwavering consumption.

Jakob asked me half-heartedly if I wanted to return to the town, and his tone pleased me because it made me feel like he didn't want me to leave, even if perhaps he was only worried I'd take Ada with me. But I said no, I would stay. They didn't exactly thank me, but Tom Vane laid off my father for a few days.

* * *

There was a spate of small fires, and then a gap of a few weeks where nothing happened. Some damp weather helped and the smell of water in the air cheered me, but like always in that place the cheer left quickly. We became agitated with the lack of activity, with the invisible threat. The horses stamped, the dogs roved and fought, Ada was restless. We asked to go riding, but Tom wouldn't let us leave in case a fire broke. I spent long nights with Jan and Isaac and Sim, lying on the settle looking at the stars, or sitting in the hut, poking hickory batons into the fire pit and watching the flames, then falling asleep in their dappling. In the daytime, we would take the half-burnt batons and use their charcoal ends to play Xs and Os on the side of the hut.

During these idle days, I began to question what I was doing there. My presence was helpful to my father, who was in debt and maybe now sick, and I knew my mother wasn't only appalled at my joining the sprawl, I could sense I played a role in one of her small battles against the town. I pictured her now at the chickens, now at the stove, a flicker of a smile on her face as she thought of me taking on a task at which the men failed steadily. I thought of dead Petr, whose cot I filled, who had burnt alive in the previous year's sprawl. I had seen his grave in a corner of the town graveyard, a wooden cross marking the spot, and his name marking the wood, and the wood likely taken from the forest that had killed him.

And maybe it was true that I enjoyed the job, being with the men, away from home and doing something important. But when I left our hut each morning, and stared down at the forests, I began to think how out of place the trees looked. I had seen the other side of the hills, I had ridden over their small peaks and looked around at the endless flat treeless nothing. This land wasn't meant for woods. It was barely meant for life. It welcomed the fire, and I wondered who had tricked us into doubting it.

I began to think I was there for no good reason. My participation had no logic, no reward. I was there because I was a part of that nature, as accidental as the trees or the dogs, or the buzzards that spun above it all.

*   *   *

Then, one night, the fires started again. We woke to the dogs barking manically, and in a blur we were on our horses plummeting down to the near woods, where flames were crawling up a pine. We got the tree down. Tom did his review and found nothing; we rewarded the dogs and were back in bed by dawn.

But the next night, another fire, also in the near woods, to the east this time. We charged it down.

And the next night, the same, at the three-year-olds – we were becoming nocturnal, waking at midnight.

The following night, another fire, one that nearly became a gorse blaze, but we managed it.

And it was the night after this that we were less lucky. The canopies of some trees in the near plots went up and began to blaze, the heat feeding on itself and the flames racing down the avenue. Finally I saw the skill of Jakob, making fire to stop fire. He made the call quickly, he shouted to Tom, who agreed, and they rode quickly down the avenue and started hacking down one tree, two trees, a third, and then Isaac came from the fire with a lit torch, passed it to Jakob, and they began the rival fire.

It worked, but not immediately. The next morning, we looked at the damage from the settle. The difference was breathtaking, a patch of trees was now absent from the view, and what took its place was a black ooze similar to a scab. In the air we smelled acid, and I wondered if the smell and the ash would travel to the town, but it rained then, dampening the air and the ash, and the rain felt at odds with the previous night's fire, and we sat in the dripping huts watching it while Tom Vane frantically searched the charred woods below us. The rain stopped after lunch, and Tom returned covered in wet ash, and he shouted nonsensical orders at us, began lashing out at the horses and then praising and caressing the dogs, rolling with them in the wet grass until they were covered in mud. We ate dinner in silence on the settle, the grass already drying, Tom with mud on his face, the air smelling of pine. That was the last time I remember smelling pine in Canada.

That night, we slept through. The air was peaceful, there was no wind, and I dreamt of my bedroom at home, flowers in my mother's arms, the lilac hem of her skirt.

But the following night, after a quiet day, I was haunted by a disgusting nightmare, one that when I thought about it afterwards made me feel close to vomiting. It was a nightmare of the kind you feel is real, and that as a result alters your perception of the real, so that friends or objects in the nightmare lose their goodness and become enemies or evil omens the next day. I woke from the nightmare to barking, another fire had broken out.

*   *   *

What did I feel that night, as we took the horses, as we headed down into those woods? There was confusion, fire was in more than one place – Jan and I were side by side, and we had to wheel around twice, follow new calls to different plots. I kept my eyes on the path in front of me, I didn't look up at the woods, at the red in the sky. Did I feel afraid? I would like to think that by then, by the final fire we faced, I had become brave.

Yes, the final fire. It seems inevitable now, but it wasn't at the time. We hadn't known that there could *be* a final one. The plan was to limit the sprawl, we had never imagined it could take everything.

We fought the flames all night, but we lost. We ran, panted, ran, hacked, and we were never close to winning, we fought with no effect on the fire, whose burn we felt all over our bodies, even deep in our stomachs. By dawn the fire had taken half the plots, and it took the rest the next day.

We sat on the settle watching the sprawl, understanding that this was the end of the forest. Tom was somewhere down there, and eventually Jakob rode to find him. When they returned, I heard Jakob say that he had found Tom in a water pit, on his knees and submerged to the waist, playing with a piece of red string and apologising. I remembered Tom in the night, hacking at random trees with a long axe. I tried to remember Ada, who hadn't returned to the settle. I thought I'd last seen her when the near plots had gone and the three-year-olds were beginning to take, and we realised we needed to get out fast because a wall of fire would soon lock us in. Horses and men were appearing and disappearing in the smoke, dogs too, and the dogs seemed to be chasing the fire still, barking at it, attacking it, their lips pulled back, their eyes rolling, their hair stiff, but didn't I also have an image – a memory or a nightmare? – of Ada, sitting calm, waiting by Tom for her reward.

* * *

We returned to the town as failures and were met with no ill will or animosity, because the town understood the failure to be its own. The Vanes closed their business, and the town foundered. Like many families, mine left, and soon we travelled to Scotland, taking the opposite route to our ancestors, another retreat.

I thought about the sprawl often. My mother liked to tell people of my time there on the settle, fighting fire with the men, and her stories tired me, they dragged at me; for many years, a dog's bark, especially at night, would bring me back there to the edge of the forests, and I would find my heart racing, the real world blurring around me.

But over time, those effects wore off, and I heard nothing of the town or of the Vanes until my eldest was fifteen, and I attended an agricultural fair in Perth. At a stall, selling a type of farming machinery, I saw Jan Vane. He was older now, and he looked stronger. He had a salesman's confidence. I said hello and asked if he remembered me, and he was polite and kind and he said he did of course.

He excused himself from the stall, and we walked through the fair, discussing his and my life. He was living now near Berwick, and also had a family. He rarely heard news of his parents' family. He believed his brother Jakob might be in Edmonton or perhaps Red Deer, but he was more certain about Tom Vane. Jan said that Tom hadn't worked again after that sprawl, he had begun drinking, had accumulated debt, and had died young in Calgary. Jan showed no remorse for his brother's death, and I didn't pretend to feel any either. Instead I felt the same cynicism, the inside smirk, that I had felt as a teenager in the forests in Canada. Rather than please me though, this smirk now depressed me. The Vanes, constantly betrayed by the nature they cultivated, are for me the sad evidence of futility.

As we came back through the fair to Jan's stall, we passed a collie puppy with a soot black coat, and Jan and I paused to look at it, evidently with similar thoughts going through our heads. Absently and in response to nothing, Jan said, 'yes,' and then he turned to face me. He began saying that it wasn't every fire, but it was some of them, and in particular the later ones, in particular the final sprawl. He said he had watched her do it, for his own reasons he hadn't stopped her. You know what I'm talking about, don't you, he said. You saw her. And I remembered what at the time I had thought was a nightmare, the one that had brought me close to vomiting, that still makes me feel sick today: my dog Ada, walking through the hut towards the door and the night outside, her face lit by the red glow of a hickory baton, one half of it on fire and the other half in her mouth.

Visitors

Hiding from them is easy.

I'm in the den, they're in the kitchen. It's Tuesday evening.

Mitch always tries to include me, his younger sister, in these midweek parties. Come on Ken, its's a whole new crew again tonight. Thanks Mitch, I think I'll pass.

So while he's doing lines and drinking Labatt's, I'm foetal on the couch with CP24 on mute, and Mom's old patterned blanket pulled up to my chin. Either side of the TV, my two expensively wrapped candles lull a low-key lavender scent from their tiny, persistent flames. Off to the side, stand photos of Mom and Dad and one of us all together as a family smiling on the beach in Aruba.

I can hear another truck drill up the yard into the knuckle of RAMs and Chargers and Ford F-150s. It's ten-fifteen. They've been arriving since eight. If many more come, they'll be forced to find space among the spare parts and write-offs growing moss round back or break through to the fenced-off customer parking next door.

Mitch is 31, five years older than me. He's gained some rubber round the hips but his arms remain teenager-thin. Keeps telling me he's joining the gym next week, then next week comes and he's put it off again. With Dad's tire and auto repair shop sold to Pete, he could build his own.

From the live feed at the corner of the screen I can see the traffic is what you'd expect for this time of night, which is to say, a lot heavier than you'd think if you're not from the GTA. The sound of a glass smashing followed by shouts and screams and general yelping laughter flows from under the kitchen door, across the hall, under again the door to the den and down the carpeted stairs to me laid out on the couch.

A few years ago, Dad put some money into renovating the kitchen exactly according to how you'd expect a business-minded man with a lot of cash and a long-dead wife (the outsized kitchen island, the tricked-out fridge freezer he never figured out how to use, the La-Z-Boy recliners facing the wall-mounted TV).

Shot, shot, shot. Shot, shot, shot. Shot, shot, shot.

You'll work the books Kenny, Dad told me, when I started to follow him and Mitch into the garage, stretching as far as I could to match my footsteps to his and trailing a wrench in the hope that one of the men working might be looking for a wrench. Go on inside Ken, he said, we're going to need you in there managing things, just like your Mom.

The ticker across the bottom of the screen has the Premier making commitments to rezone big chunks of land for development north of Toronto. That could mean literally anywhere.

They've turned up the volume in the kitchen. Before I heard only the thrum of rolling bass, now I'm getting trebly synths and hip-hop high hats from whatever off the shelf party mix that Mitch selected for tonight's festivities.

Mom got the quick cancer and died when I was five. It was Janey with her highlights and year-round flip flops, Lauren in her dungarees, and the pack a day smokers Tina, Patty and Marlene that showed me debit and credit and adjustments for tax. I'd sit adjacent to the scrum, eye-counting the pile of cash in the centre of the table and inhaling the second-hand smoke, ready to jump if they held out a mug and said coffee hun. Always remember, they told me, this business is built on winter tires, so make sure you tell everyone you meet that those all-seasons are just a con.

Dad let me take over the books full-time the final year of high-school, after Janie left to enjoy her golden years in Florida. I kept those books tight too, never allowing a tax return to leave us out of pocket, or an invoice unaccounted for. And this is how it remained for years, until Mitch, just as soon as he found out he was going to be made power of attorney per the will, signed it all away for a song and a cash advance ten days after that Queb 18-wheeler minced Dad's truck. It fell to me to tell Tag and Brennan and the other boys who built the place up with Dad there was no point coming back.

It's been five months and I'm still waiting for my half of the inheritance. With the money from Dad's RRSPs, TFSA, his condos downtown and the land up north, I make it a million-two each easy. Mitch says his hands are tied and its all with the lawyers but I'm wise to that. I know the real truth is he's afraid once it's drawn down, I'm going to bounce.

Screeching laughter of girls likely much younger than me. Each week they get closer to high school age. Like I say to Mitch, we've become the open house for area kids who want to get high.

Before Dad died, Mitch used to party with people I knew, the sullen remnants of the hockey and high school crowd who never left. Sometimes even Tag and the boys would stop by for beers and poker. Now when I pass by the hallway to go upstairs, I hear them say, who's that, is that your sister, why doesn't she come join.

When I was sixteen, I saw Tag get in a fight outside a Shoeless Joes. He more than held is own, and when I walked up to him afterwards, and we said hello, he smiled and handed me the cigarette that he'd just lit. I let him watch me smoke it until I could feel it burn my lips. I came back the next weekend in a new tank top, but he was with a girl a few years older than me that I didn't recognize.

The news channel is getting deep into a story on opioid use in schools. There's an on-location reporter with a frantic haircut freezing outside a school at night and cuts to interviews with kids from earlier in the day, all while a banner tracking underneath demands answers to the obvious and urgent questions.

Your name is Mackenzie not Ken, don't let anyone tell you different, Mom would say. At least, that's what I have her telling me as a memory, but I was too young for that to be real. The framed photos confirm an outline: her straight white teeth, red lipstick, tan arms. And I'm pretty sure she leaned over to kiss my cheek on that family vacation in Aruba and each night in bed at home before I went to sleep. I bet she had her bad points too.

The sound of something large, like a laptop falling on kitchen tiles. For a minute, perfect silence, until someone's phone replaces the laptop as the source of the beats to the Bluetooth speaker, and the party if anything is raised to a new level of intensity.

Traffic on the 401 is finally starting to lighten up, and we've transitioned to the nightly news team of Larissa and Chris. She's my age with earnest teeth, he's Dad's and far too heavily made up. It looks like he's constantly coming up with clever quips.

A few weeks after Dad died, Tag and Brennan came by to help sort through what could be salvaged for Pete's yard from the strewn about rims, pockmarked fenders, and orphaned axles. I watched them from my upstairs window. Tag carefully sifting with the digger, Brennan lifting more than its safe to lift, Mitch relegated to gesticulating bystander. When I invited them in for a beer after they'd finished, Tag looked at Mitch then back to me and said sorry its late. Me too, said Brennan and they left.

A week later, I texted Tag and Brennan to see how they were making out with finding a job. Tag texted back that evening and we kind of started chatting. His ex Lindsay's living at her Mom's place since last fall and they're sharing custody of the kid. It can't be easy on his own, and since its not like I've much going on and its not far, I go over and run the laundry for him some days, and some nights when he's not on kid duty I go over there too.

The door at the top of the stairs is shoved in, and a boy and a girl – could be late teens – rush in. She has her back to him, and smiling, takes his hands and guides them under her cut-off top. They're laughing and they don't notice me. Then the girl gets on her knees and pulls at his belt buckle and zip. He staggers forward til his hand finds the wall.

There's probably more of them upstairs fucking on my own bed. I need to get out of here. I leave the television on and the candles to burn out as I run up the stairs, passing the young couple, who are now too busy wrapping their legs around each other to notice me.

I hurry through the hallway, not risking a glance towards the glass-panel kitchen door. The bass throbs at full boom, I can't make out the song. I slide into my Uggs and leave by the side door, my winter coat trailing behind me.

The air smells cold and suddenly I'm blinking from the edge of the porch up into the night sky, which is clear and arranged in the obvious pattern. No one's impressed with you anymore Big Dipper. I zip my coat up as far as it goes and blow air into the collar to warm up. I pad my pockets for my vape and phone and the latest five hundred I swiped from Mitch's stash of the cash advance that he keeps in a cargo box under his bed.

Maybe I can take a walk until the party is past its peak.

I skirt around the parked cars and trucks and stop at the road that links the highway to the north and the creeping surburbs to the south. Dad said the fields would be paved over by the time he'd kick. Now we have surburban kids doing coke or ketamine or worse with his first born son in the kitchen he blew thousands on.

I walk north. Either side of me, glistening fields of winter corn yawn their best impressions of fog onto the silver road. Weak streetlights hang from poles leaning at arthritic angles.

I drop the cornfields and gain roadside century homes in generous lots. The aggressive orderliness of the gardens tells you all you need to know about life one rung below the level of very comfortably well off. Money pits, Dad called them.

The freight train sends a reminder out across the fields that its working late, and there's the scurry of something small and specific near my feet. I take out my vape and inhale deeply, then blow a purple blueberry cloud to walk through.

When I was five, Mitch would take me out back to pick through the old steering wheels and car seats to build our own pretend IndyCar racer. It was fun having a brother who wanted to play with me. When I was seven, I caught him sitting cross legged rolling a joint in Mom and Dad's old bed. Then, when I was nine, I walked in on him with the bone china tea tray from the set that Gramma gave Mom as a wedding gift on his lap, portioning out the powder from one large ziplock back into a row of mini polys. Now we're all grown up, I sweep the counters clean on stale afternoons while he's still sleeping it off.

Houses all about me now. Fat nineties split levels mixed in with the florid old shacks. The porch lights are on, but I can't see any sign of life, just crouching German SUVs at rest, primed for the next morning commute. I take the left turn down the hill of the concession road.

I used to know a girl who lived here, what was her name, butch type who cried in math, Sally…Stefanovich. Chased Matty Dunlop out of a party for taking the last slice of pizza. I find a fallen pinecone and throw it at what might have once been her bedroom window. I try a second and a third, the final one cracking off glass. Seeing a light come on in the window in the room beside the one I hit, I quicken to a trot, the back of my hand covering a cough.

Blueberry breath warms the zipped-up collar of my coat. Behind me, the engine of a truck throttles to a stop at the crest of the hill. Soon its headlights are reaching ahead of me, casting my legs in long shadows. I don't look behind but put my vape back in my front pocket and pull my hood up. The shadows lose definition as the headlights are lowered to dim.

I keep to an even pace when I begin to feel the heat of the truck coming up behind me. Two, possibly three male voices whisper something quick.

Hey guy, one of them says out loud and I assume to me.

I don't answer but my pace picks up.

What you walking out here for guy?

I don't answer.

Dude, it's a *girl*.

No way.

I don't look back. I'm walking fast as I can walk.

Hey missy, do you know where that loser Mitchy Watts of the world-famous Watts Tire and Auto Repair lives?

I pull the threads of my hood tight until its squeezing into my cheeks. They rev the engine but don't come upsides.

Come on eh, we won't bite, they say.

Finally, I run, a steady makeable run to the bridge over the shallow creek.

Bitch is deaf eh, one of them says, and the headlights come on again lighting up the bridge ahead and the road that curves to the highway beyond.

I run down to the water away from the road as they thunder across the bridge. A squashed can of Old Milwaukee lands in the brown wet grass near my feet. The sound of the truck's engine soon melds into the general low-volume roar of highway traffic, soothing and imprecise like surf breaking and crashing on a banked strip of sand.

The waves falling on the beach in Aruba when Mom leaned down to kiss me. I remember it even if it didn't happen. I clench and unclench my fists and take a couple long slow vapes. It takes me a few minutes to realize that I'm shaking.

Even if they didn't see my face, and they're going the wrong way, they might find the house and tell Mitch what they saw. If he's not too far gone, he'll start yelling Kenny come here and lead a search party down to the den to drag me back to the kitchen. Why you got to be so serious K, he'd say, and shove me into the dancing circle formed to jump and shout around me, with me turning in every direction, watching for hands from the crowd that grab and pinch.

Her smiling bright teeth and her warm breath when she kissed my cheek on the beach in the blinding sun. Your name is Mackenzie not Ken.

The reeds stand stiff in the shallow water that will in a few weeks turn to ice. I hopscotch across the sludge that accumulates at the base of the sturdiest clumps. My Uggs are a friggin mess but my feet are still dry. I lean into the steep incline until I'm in yet another flat field of still standing corn. I find the lines and make my way through.

Mitch wouldn't come to identify Dad. I can't, he said, bottle in hand and his back to me. Okay, Mitch. I alone get to see that big face swollen and jumbled all up in bits.

Dad was pretty fucking useless after Mom died too. I'd watch him through doors left ajar as he stirred his sugar too far into his morning coffee. It was worse at night, when he would come sit on the edge of the bed and place his huge hand on my small back for a long time, saying nothing and possibly crying, before laying on the bed behind me and finally sleep with his heavy arm over my shoulder. I'd have to wriggle out from under the weight to the cool edge of the mattress where the worst of his cigarette and Sunny Delight cut vodka breath didn't reach.

The winter corn ends and the ground dips before rising again to road. I've seen deer in this hollow stooping low to lick the salt runoff. Facing me is the last house left on this particular sideroad. Behind it run parcelled out quadrants of broken ground, prepped for the off the shelf townhouses, cookie cutter mansions and strip malls to come.

The light is on in the front room and the curtains are not pulled. A young girl is sitting at a table drinking a glass of milk. Her hair is blond like mine and her pyjamas are black and red plaid with a white neck frill. She's drawing something, yes, there's a marker or pencil or paintbrush in her hand and she's scrawling with it across whatever's in front of her in between taking long sips from the glass of milk.

She looks in my direction. She cannot see me, but her mouth is open and her eyes are wide and she's pointing a finger in my direction. I know what it's like to sense something at night in the reflection of a well-lit room, where you can see only hints from the black night beyond.

She drinks her milk and yawns slowly. Tag appears then and sneaks up behind her and lifts her in one quick whooshing movement onto his shoulder.

She's climbing all over him and kicking her legs but it's a giddy act with giggles from her and laughs from him. They leave the part of the room visible through the window. Then the light in the front room goes off and a light upstairs comes on.

I text him "sorry but I had to come" and wait to see if the screen door opens to the catch. The upstairs light is off now and then a weaker light like a bedside lamp flicks on for a minute, before the whole house goes dark.

I walk out onto the centre of the road. No cars have passed and no headlights can be seen now, the recently re-marked and streetlit road looks like it's part of a display for whatever's yet to come. But there's always some movement somewhere on the grid: a hoarse old pickup rattles loud then fades from one of the sideroads parallel. There's no big secret here to getting ahead or breaking out. It's straight flat land in all directions, ready and waiting for the money to be poured right in.

The screen door swings open to the catch.

I walk to it, pull it free and bring it in slowly behind me, pushing the unlocked inside door with my elbow at the same time. I slide out of my Uggs, and place them on the mat beside the work boots. There's a pair of kid's winter boots on the mat that I'm not used to seeing.

I can make out the stairs in the darkness. I gently place my socked feet on each step to dampen unwanted creaks. At the top, I turn right towards the door that's ajar. Walking on my toes now, and holding my breath, I'm through that doorway too. I replace the door to a fully closed position and quietly exhale.

Okay Kenz? whispers Tag.

I'm sorry T.

I reach for the nightstand and count down with my fingers to the third drawer. I remove from the pocket of my winter jacket, the five one-hundred dollar bills from Mitch's stash and place them in the drawer with the others.

Tag's pulls the covers down at the far side of the bed so that a triangle of mattress is showing. I walk around to that side, letting my jacket fall to the floor, and pinch my socks off with my fingers and sit down on the bed with my back to him.

I'll be gone before she wakes up, I say.

Let's just sleep, everything's going to be okay, he says, and holds the covers up for me, waiting until my head is on the pillow to tuck them right up to my ears. His arm comes around again then to keep the covers snug to my neck for the night. Soon his slow breathing tells me he's asleep.

There's close to nine-thousand two in Tag's nightstand drawer. Not even close to the severance he's owed but it's a start. Mitch isn't going to miss it anyways, when he can't even remember who's winning at poker.

I look through curtains that never meet over the cornfield that I've walked across, then on up the hill to the sleeping houses and the road out of the hamlet to where Mitch and his temporary leeches will be partying against the night. Down then to the den with the TV still on and the candles burning in front of the photos of Mom and Dad. The flame burns down to the wrapping paper they came packaged in. A weak, dying flame like that is always more likely to end its journey there. But if it takes, how quick a flame can really take, quicker than a cough or sneeze its off to the races, flaring from the wrapping paper down to the empty pizza boxes that I used to sit the candles on, and on to the stacks of Dad's old autotrader magazines to the overloaded outlets and wires that have their inside colours showing. The nightly news crew continue to smile as the wires spark and the flames lick and the fire – it's a fire now not a flame – finds the wooden frame of the basement wall and rebounds up the ceiling. From there, its only option is to swerve upward out of the den and into the hallway, relentless and strong and ready for the night.

MOHINI SINGH

Starlings

The girl hasn't stopped crying since they left the hospital. What did she expect? A miracle? But if Tripti were to say anything — two words of consolation, five words of advice — she'll only be met with another bout of tears. Or worse, a fit of rage. Better to stay quiet and watch her daughter's tears stream like rain. Tripti wishes Varun was here. He said he'd finish work early and come straight to the hospital. Even as he promised her, taking her hand into his own calloused ones, she knew he was lying; yet, waiting in the sterile, purgatorial whiteness of the hospital corridor, she hoped he would come. She'd never felt so lonely. Back home, back in India, she wouldn't have been so easily abandoned. Back home, this wouldn't have happened at all. But Tripti can't quite tell if that was because of India or because she would have been a different person there.

Odd business that, moving to a new country, when you were only twenty. Just when you were learning to be your own person — average height, above average beauty, a sharp mind — you were slapped with a language which hadn't the letter to sound your name; clouds which hadn't heard of monsoon and didn't know how to bide their time; and pounds and pence which felt so much lighter than they were worth. What do you do then with the first twenty years? Throw them out? Store them away? Adapt, Varun would say. His mantra from the moment they had landed at Heathrow and travelled, not too far, barely fifteen minutes in the taxi, to a narrow street with identical pebble-dashed houses, overgrown front gardens and mossy roof tiles. They had set up their lives in one such house where they still live twenty years on. Odd business.

'How do they know which direction to turn?' asks Richa, tears momentarily stopped, looking up at the murmuration of starlings in the shape of a large comma. 'They must really trust each other.'

Tripti looks up briefly. She doesn't like being distracted on the M25. It's taken her a long time to adapt to driving. She checks her rear-view and wing mirror again. All good. No weaving motorcyclist. She turns up the heating to clear the smidgen of condensation on the windshield and settles back into the middle lane at 60mph, already having forgotten her daughter's question.

'Should I tell him about the baby?' Richa asks.

Tripti's skin burns with fury. Any mention of that man fills her with murderous rage. Recently, she's seen him hanging around the usual places: the park, the bus stop, by the corner shop, smoking, laughing with his friends. No regret at bringing shame upon his family; no fear of being out on bail with the prospect of going back to prison. Will he go back, though? Will they convict him? Back home, she would've paid the policemen to beat him to within an inch of his life, then some more, until he confessed. Here, with no recourse to bribery and no trust in the colour blindness of the judicial system, she wishes him to be run over by a lorry and be confined to his bed, shitting in his pants for the rest of his life or be mauled by a pack of dogs, ripped apart, chunk by chunk. She knows herself to be an unforgiving person so doesn't lose any sleep over wishing such vengeance upon that man. If anything, she regrets her limited imagination.

'He'd want to know,' Richa pushes.

'I don't give a toss what that man does or doesn't want. And who knows if the baby was really his?' Tripti says, unwilling to suffer alone. A hiccupy gasp from Richa and she knows the remark has cut deep, but she receives no satisfaction from it.

It happens five miles later, just as Tripti indicates to exit the motorway. They fall like black hail. The noise a sickening gloop. One splatters on the windshield; the impact not enough to kill it immediately. Its small yellow beak opens and closes as it gasps for morsels of air. Before she knows it, Tripti's finger has flicked the wiper toggle and the starling's tiny body begins to paint a bloody and feathery picture on the glass. Richa screams and screams.

*   *   *

It's rained all night; a fine, winter drizzle which nudges Tripti's dream to weave through warm memories of summer holidays. A yellow, cotton frock; milk lolly in hand, run along the river; a splash in the pond behind *nani*'s house; the mango tree which waited on the other side. Tripti wakes up with her mind still stretching towards the overladen branches of the tree. She makes breakfast, washes the dishes and tidies up the living room. She expects Richa to help, but the girl has been near catatonic since the incident on the motorway. What if she doesn't speak at all during the interview? Varun fixes these meetings and then disappears, leaving Tripti to answer personal questions from strangers. *Adapt*, she shouts at him when he returns in the middle of the night, face streaked and puffy from crying in his cousin's kitchen. Tripti would rather die than step in that

121

kitchen, that house again. She'd rather gouge her eyes out than lay them on that tart of a niece who had exposed her innocent Richa to the alternative life of cheap attention and favours. Tripti had babysat the niece, fed her, knitted her jumpers, ultimately, she had trusted her. But look how she's been repaid: with a daughter with a stain on her character. And instead of admitting her mistake, the niece now sells her shame to journalists and reporters. Then sends them two houses down to Tripti's pebble-dash house with windows boarded up against hurled stones.

The doorbell rings. Tripti sighs, brushes down her blouse and opens the door.

Another woman. This one is called Kerry. She's doing a newspaper feature and has interviewed six other girls so far. Half of them in the neighbouring town. Tripti didn't know the ring extended to other towns. The bastards!

Before she steps away from the door, she widens her eyes and gives Kerry a full stare. Her way of eliminating the scandal-hungry reporters, the ones looking to sensationalise her daughter's humiliation. They can barely meet her eyes, but this one holds Tripti's stare. A touch of honesty in those deep blue discs. She lets her in.

Kerry scrubs her shoes on the mat, leaving balls of purple feather and flesh, like something coughed up by a cat. They both look at it for a moment, then, to be extra sure, Kerry takes off her shoes. She is seated on the good chair with the freshest upholstery and waits for Richa, while Tripti makes tea. There will be no small talk, for Tripti has neither the skill nor the patience for it. TV must fill the silence, as it has always done in her house, when, after a long day at work — threading, waxing, tinting eyelashes, painting nails — and cleaning and cooking once home, she has no strength left to make sense of anything else. Life outside her tired body turns into a documentary, like an episode of *Most Amazing Steam Trains*, that she can dip in and out of but never quite engage with. Perhaps that's where she went wrong.

Kerry is looking at a file, while stealing glances at the living room. Everything second-hand from St Christopher's on the high street: the two-seater sofa; shoe cabinet stuffed full of trainers and broken flip-flops; chipped, glass coffee table; even the generic landscapes which Tripti had bought in the hope that they might be lost treasures. But the mandir she got custom made to house her bronze Ganesha which she'd carried all the way from India. So long she's prayed to the obstacle-remover and this is how he blesses her: turning her into a social outcast. Well, now he can just sit there and collect dust. Tripti has no time for him anymore. She hands a *World's Best Mum* mug to Kerry and turns to the TV where two young women and a middle-aged man are talking about the recent natural disaster — the fall of the starlings — while sitting on a nice yellow sofa which wouldn't even fit in her living room. The way they're going on about it, it might as well be the end of the world. A few starlings falling from the sky has got the whole bloody country up in arms, but a dozen teenage girls being raped day after day for a year is pushed to page 5.

It's the shame. The humiliation of a dozen girls reeks. What to do but hold your nose, eh?

Richa is here, in a fresh set of clothes, thank god. Kerry is on her feet with a smile of one who's learned it by gritting her teeth through difficult times and extends both hands to shake Richa's. The girl responds with her own open smile and Tripti feels lighter. She leaves them to it. There's a limit to how many times a mother can listen to her daughter's ordeal. But she keeps an ear out for anything that might make Richa feel uncomfortable. She has sent packing many reporters until now; her current record stands at forty-seven seconds.

But this one is different; she felt that from the moment Kerry walked into the house. A sense of being part of their misfortune, not just looking at it from the outside. Perhaps it is just an act? Yet, her questions are different. Not *how* it happened but *why*. Not *where* but *who*. Not *what Richa did* but *what she will do*. And Richa talks, albeit slowly, guardedly, waiting for that barbed question which will eventually pin all the blame on her.

'He was different from the others.' Richa looks at her mother, then out of the boarded window, at her memory of the view outside. Was it of the library where she went after school and which Tripti didn't know had shut down two years ago? Or the derelict house "awaiting demolition as part of a regeneration scheme" which currently generated druggies? 'Others were kind only in the beginning,' Richa says after a while. 'Then they turned nasty. But he ... he cared for me. He made me feel different, you know?'

Kerry nods. 'How?'

Richa is quiet.

'He made you feel special? Like you were the only one?' Kerry suggests.

'No. Not special. More like ... needed. Like I wasn't unnecessary. There was a reason for my existence too, which was to make him happy.'

The tea sours in Tripti's mouth. This is the first she's heard of this. What does the girl mean? Everyone is necessary to some extent and equally unnecessary. Does the world stop revolving because of one person? Will the sun not rise tomorrow if Tripti were to suddenly disappear? Yes, her husband will miss her food, her company, perhaps, but did that make her necessary? Does God expect us to become necessary by making *TikTok* videos or to simply do our duty?

'Did he make you happy?' Kerry persists.

Tripti likes this one. She likes her very much.

'Sometimes,' Richa replies.

'Did he know you were only fourteen when he started the relationship?' Richa nods.

The bell rings. School boys at the door. One throws water in Tripti's face and screams, 'Slut!' before running away, laughing. Tripti shuts the door gently. She will not slam it; she will not lose her dignity. She wipes her face with the tea-towel and sits back down at the kitchen table. Has she reported these incidents to the police? Kerry asks. She has, many times, but they're scared, lest they too start reeking of the shame.

'Where we come from,' she says, 'we were the highest caste. But now we've become the untouchables. We must adapt to this new status.'

'It's all my fault,' says Richa, holding back a sob.

'Get that notion out of your head,' Kerry says, a touch too sharply. Then, in a softer tone, 'Nothing about this sordid business is your fault.'

'Tell that to my mum,' Richa snaps. 'She thinks I've done this deliberately to upset her perfectly boring life.'

Boring! The girl flings that word around willy-nilly. *The chickpeas are boring. The Ford Fiesta is boring. A long weekend in Blackpool is boring.* She means it as an insult, but to Tripti it's a sign of a steady life.

'Was the excitement worth the cost?' she retorts.

'See!' Tears roll down Richa's face. 'She hates me. She can barely look at me.'

Kerry shakes her head in disappointment and Tripti feels a rush of anger. She rebukes herself for not speaking in Hindi. She rebukes herself again for wanting to hide her thoughts from this woman. Who was she to judge her? Can she even understand the humiliation Tripti feels after all she has done for the thankless girl? How let-down she feels? Or... or how guilty? If she had been around more, gone shopping with Richa, watched a film with her, done less boring things, would her daughter have come to her sooner? Confided in her earlier? Would this have happened at all?

A plane flies over the house. Low. Just taking off. Tripti feels the engine vibrate inside her body.

'Airbus,' she says. When Kerry frowns, she adds, 'It makes a whiny sound on take-off. Boeing growls.'

In twenty years, she's learned to listen to the subtle differences in aeroplanes but not to her own daughter.

She makes another cup of tea and heats up some halwa she had made the day before. Kerry eats a spoonful and declares it delicious. Probably just being polite, Tripti thinks, but she can't help feeling proud.

'Why do you think they're falling?' Richa asks, having composed herself too with her mother's halwa.

The TV is playing a recording of a large murmur of starlings falling to their deaths on the green fields of Cotswolds. It flicks to a view of Hyde Park with dead starlings floating in the Serpentine. Then to a traffic jam caused by a lorry skidding over a carpet of crushed birds.

'I'm not sure,' says Kerry. 'But I think it's got something to do with the Earth's magnetic field. When they fly, they use each other as markers. But sometimes, they lose their bearing; if they're attacked, for example. Although, this is happening only in the UK. Starlings elsewhere are fine.'

'Do you know there's no evolutionary reason for starlings to murmurate? They do it for the sheer joy of it,' Richa says. 'So if they're now falling, it's because they're killing themselves. Mass suicide.' She looks challengingly at her mother who's trying hard not to show the shock in her face. 'They're sick of us humans treating their home, nature, badly, so they're protesting. There's a twitter account: @DeadBirdsTellNoTails. It's funny. You should check it out.' But she doesn't laugh; instead, she digs her nails in the soft of her palm. A new habit. 'There have been many cases of animal suicide, you know. In *The Giaour*, Byron wrote of the scorpion which, when surrounded by fire, stings itself: "And maddening in her ire / One sad and sole relief she knows / The sting she nourished for her foes."'

She's showing off. *See how clever I am? So it couldn't possibly be my fault what happened to me.* Or: *I'm so clever everything that happened was by choice. I am definitely not stupid.* And she isn't, that's why it was such a shock. Intelligent, eloquent, ambitious. Where did it all go wrong?

'Dolphins in captivity who refuse to resurface. Or aphids who explode to save their colony,' Richa continues, warming to her topic. 'Most common example are human beings. Wars are nothing but mass suicides. To limit the population. Self-destruction for future preservation.'

Kerry is listening intently. Is she buying this crap? English Lit excuse for a life destroyed.

Richa suddenly laughs. No mirth; more like the wretched whine of a wounded puppy. Then says, 'Maybe that's why my baby died. To preserve me.'

Tripti is unloading the dishwasher. The plate in her hand falls and breaks into three large pieces. Sighing, she picks them up and puts the white slices together on the table, in a near-image of the original. Even if she glues them together, the cracks will still be visible.

Kerry wants to know how the baby died.

'My mother killed it.'

The boiler kicks in with a loud clang and the pipes hiss. The walls make a deep humming sound. Kerry stares at Tripti, but there is nothing to say. The girl will believe what she wants to.

'She said to me that had we been in India, she would have forced me to have an abortion or married me to an old widower. A few days later, I fell down the stairs and lost the baby. She pushed me.' Richa's finger extends dramatically towards Tripti.

So much easier to believe her version because it's far more dramatic than the mundane truth, bolstered by those awful words Tripti had flung at her. Richa had screamed the accusation repeatedly at the hospital too, until the nurses took Tripti aside to have a quiet word. She told them what she tells Kerry now: 'The girl tripped over the wire of the vacuum cleaner.'

'Liar!'

Tripti wants to turn around to see Kerry's expression, to know who she believes, but it's so tiring to be judged and blamed. Another accusatory look will push her over the edge.

'The other girls,' Kerry says, 'including your cousin, have agreed to testify against the men. Would you consider doing the same?'

'No.'

'May I ask why?'

'I love him. And he loves me. When I messaged him about the baby,' she looks at her mother defiantly, 'he promised me that when all this is over, he'll take me away from here. We'll live together in love. We'll start our own family.'

Tripti laughs bitterly. To hide her anger, her impotency. Do you see, Kerry? Do you see now? This is the crap I have to put up with. Before any of you judge me, listen to my daughter's maddening aspirations. This is why I cradle strangers' feet in my lap and buff their nails and file their corns so my daughter can start a family at sixteen. Tripti slams the three broken pieces of the plate into the bin, smashing them to dusty bits.

Kerry takes the girl's hand in hers and squeezes it. In her eyes, Tripti sees nothing but love for her young, emotional and intelligent daughter. 'I'm afraid that's one hope you'll have to give up,' says Kerry. 'He is going back to prison. All of them are, for a long, long time. I'll make sure of that. It's a promise I've made to all the other girls.'

Richa gasps, pulls her hand away and brings them to her mouth. She shrinks back into her armchair and sobs. Tripti has seen people do that on TV; she thought only actors cried like that. But the sight of her own daughter trembling in the middle of patchwork upholstery, tears and snot running down her dress, darkening long-faded colours, coupled with the words spoken by Kerry releases something in Tripti. Smothered under layers and layers of shame, laid down afresh each night by her own hands; a purgatorial shame of abandoning the ways of her previous life, while never having a firm grip on her new one, only exhausting attempts to adapt. Yet, chiselling their way out of these hardened layers, emerge: love and hope.

* * *

The full feature is published in The Times and extracts in other newspapers.

Shame of a Country

It's almost as if, after a year, this is the first time the nation's heard of it. MPs scream in the parliament about the girls' wound which hasn't even begun to scab over. Radio 4 interviews one expert after another, as though the scandal was an unfathomable mess which could only be explained through expert knowledge and not simply a ring of paedophiles preying on vulnerable girls and overlooked by the police. Tripti only listens when they interview Kerry.

And the starlings keep falling.

On the day of the hearing, a large group of women gather outside the court, chanting slogans and raising banners about police incompetence and women's protection. Behind them, the street sweepers pile up the dead birds which haven't already been eaten by the city's many cats. Tripti is there early with Richa, without Varun. He has failed to adapt to this. They sit beside Kerry, and soon the pew-like benches are filled with 15- to16-year-old girls. Richa watches them walking in one by one and grabs her mother's hand. It's one thing to read about their ordeal in Kerry's report but something else altogether to see those betrayed eyes set grimly in innocent, child-like faces. Each girl nods at Richa and the others as she walks past, with or without a parent. Towards Kerry their eyes are grateful. The niece arrives at the end. When she sees Tripti, her eyes lower, but Tripti pats the empty spot beside her invitingly.

The trial continues for two weeks, and every day those girls are there and Tripti and Richa and Kerry. The girls tell their story, one by one, with superhuman composure even when every eye in the public area is wet. Richa is marvellous, but she doesn't look at him once. At the end of the two weeks, each and every one of those men is sentenced to at least ten years in prison. It's only then that the girls allow themselves to cry and hug each other in joyous victory. But Richa stands away from them, still holding her mum's hand.

They had lost their bearing, mother and daughter, flew away from each other and crashed. But they've found one another again. Be the other's marker; guiding, no matter how far away they fly. The shape of their bond will change, murmurate, but they'll glide through it together. With love. Without shame.

They step outside to a loud cheer. A flock of starlings brooding in the nearby tree take to the sky. Tripti and Richa watch the black cloud change fluidly from a tear to a wave to a petal to the curve of an eye.

RADHIKA MAIRA TABREZ

Steel Glass

The way they sit on the bench – two silhouettes blended into one, framed by the bright orange and yellow – it is hard to tell where Bindiya ends and Jayanti begins.

Bindiya, in her polyester saree; shriveled with lack of care, hanging a few inches above her ankles. Tattered hem of the petticoat peeking out. Pallu, slipping off her shoulders, bringing the loose blouse off with it, exposing her scrawny collarbone. She doesn't bother fixing it though. She never did.

Jayanti, in an expensive South Cotton saree. A dull beige-colored drape. Every fold of the saree, every pleat, well in place. Presentable, even when in pain. Dignified, even when daunted. Like she has always been.

The air around them is dense with smoke, muting every sound. It is a quiet night, at the end of what feels like a whole year of being stunned into silence. Bindiya and Jayanti sit there in their cocoon. The two women, the smoke, and the stillness; with only the snap and crackle of the fire piercing it every now and then.

They say the soul doesn't leave the body until the fire is completely extinguished. Does that mean he is still here? She can still see the body's dark contours in the canopy of flames. His clothes still hang behind the bathroom door. The mattress still reeks of the countless cigarettes over the years; and now also of his sweat and urine from the last few days. It may be a while before he is gone. Fully gone. The loudest thought in the chaos that is Jayanti's mind at the moment, is how this wormhole of limbo, a smelly mattress, and these dancing flames in her pupils are all that is left of the last thirty years of her life.

All Bindiya can think of is the table. Barely visible now, in the dense flames. The only table she could afford came with wobbly legs. Every morning, before starting the day's work, she would turn it over and hammer in the nails that had come loose, with a block of cement. The table would continue to squeak, still, but softer. Bindiya is thinking of a life lived under the steady tempo of that squeaking. Chooon-chooon. Chooon-chooon. Chooon-chooon; when she'd put the box iron on it. Chooon-chooon; when she'd take it off. Chooon-chooon, chooon-chooon, chooon-chooon when her husband – drunk out of his wits – would climb

129

atop her in the middle of the night. All she could ever think of, as he ravaged her, was how would she manage the next day's ironing if the table's legs gave up. They never did though; loyal companions. They will, finally; any moment now. By morning, everything will be ash. The table. Its squeaky legs. The last fifteen years of her life. And all Bindiya would have left to show for it would be that block of cement.

A loud pop of ember explodes, bringing a thought to Jayanti like a bolt of lightning in a quiet sky, "Where would you sleep now?"

"Ground," Bindiya cocks her head in the general direction of her hut at the far end of the park, and then taps the bench they are sitting on. "Or here."

A shiver runs down Jayanti's spine. She has heard the rumors over the years; too many to ignore. A widow, in the prime of her life, sleeping on a park bench. No one ever blamed the men.

Jayanti takes a gander around the park's periphery. It is a pretty neat, typical suburban formation. Twenty houses in a square arrangement with a communal park in the middle. A solid phantasm of a sense of community. She can see her neighbors' shadows dotting the balconies. All those people should be here with her. On this bench. In this smoke and heat. The ones too shocked to walk away are still standing there. Or perhaps, they have nothing better to do. It is hard to say these days. After a year spent locked inside any kind of a show is entertainment. Even something as macabre as this.

Most of the remonstrations had died down an hour ago anyway; not long after they had started. There is no end these days, to what people will allow themselves to get used to. Besides, in a world that objects too much, to almost everything, protests must be portioned small and dished out perfunctorily. Some people had then started making videos on their phones. Bizarre is the hottest currency these days; humanity and its deplorable state documented in viral videos on TikTok. Everyone wants as much as they can grab. Jayanti's video might even make it to tomorrow's news! Or it won't. Who knows what is abnormal enough for these times. For this year. After all that has happened. Is still happening.

The fire is going strong. Surprisingly, a full outline of a human body is still visible, albeit a bit curved in the middle. Jayanti had read once that fire causes the soft tissues to contract on burning, which in turn causes the joints to flex. As a result, human bodies, when burned, often contort into what is known as a boxer pose. This is the only proof of any kind of softness in her husband that she has seen in the last thirty years. She leans on her right arm to adjust her posture; this evening hasn't been easy on her knees. Something pricks her palm. A splinter. From dragging the old chairs. One never sees a splinter till it is lodged deep inside their skin. And the fact of the matter is, rotten wood that can give a splinter never gives only one. Scabs dot Jayanti's body and soul. What is another one? It's the last one, anyway.

So what if he is a lot older, they had all said.

All that talk about his first wife is only rumors. She died from injuries from falling down the stairs... Slipped, not pushed, of course!

He will provide for you. You will be happy. Trust us.

Words are cheap. Assurances that one doesn't have to answer for later, even cheaper.

Jayanti looks at the burning body, then the splinter, and tightens her fist.

"We should make some tea." She stands up with a snap. Her knee revolts. But surprisingly, her voice feels new; fuller. The fire wouldn't take long now. It's almost over. She can feel it in the pit of her stomach, perhaps where that timbre stemmed from.

Bindiya gets up too but waits, her body turned away from the fire, her face turned towards it. It is about to happen. She can feel the quiver of the table's legs in hers.

Jayanti walks all the way up to the park gate and stops a few feet away from Bindiya's hut. Bindiya deserves some time alone with the fire. In a way, Bindiya has lost more in this fire than Jayanti ever even had.

Jayanti scans the insides of the hut. 'Hut' is a stretch, though. More of a corrugated tin roof, thrown over the five-foot-high walls of the park's stone boundary on one side and held up on the other two sides by a wall made of all sorts of things. Logs, bamboo, pieces of metal, tarp. Whatever Bindiya could find and fit in. No fourth wall, though. No door either. Only a ragged bedsheet slung over a rope as a makeshift curtain, offering no safety or privacy. People like Bindiya don't get either of those. A few years ago she had saved up some money and requested permission to build proper brick-and-mortar walls and install a wooden door. The Residents' Committee had threatened to pull down the whole structure if she ever did.

Jayanti looks at the tin roof, trying to imagine how it must sizzle during the summer. Bindiya; spending her days trapped between two scorching worlds. One that feeds her - the box iron; and the other that keeps her sheltered - the tin roof. Barely, though, both of them. What a relief the cold cement of the park bench must feel like then, to Bindiya's back. She was never allowed the safety of a door; she might as well enjoy the breeze on the bench! Jayanti gets that. Not that any of the men ever succeeded anyway. Some even walked away with a good thrashing.

A loud thump makes Jayanti turn around.

She can see Bindiya filling up the distance between them; her steps are heavy. Behind Bindiya Jayanti can see that the table has finally collapsed. The body is now lying on the ground. The flames are rapturous.

*　*　*

They return twenty minutes later. A chorus of fresh gasps follows the sound of the melamine tray sliding onto the cement bench. The crowd is galvanized. Shadows leaning over the railings – languorous and detached – are now taut and attentive. Just the response they had expected. Bindiya snickers. Jayanti breathes in deep and heavy, sits down, picks up the cup and the saucer, leans back, and lets the small of her back meet the cold cement of the bench's backrest. She likes it.

Bindiya pulls one of her legs up on the bench, hugs the knee with one arm, picks up the steel glass, wraps her saree's pallu around it, and brings it close to her nose. Always a steel glass for her, never a cup and a saucer. Actually, people like her don't get offered tea in cups and saucers. Or, any tea at all, for that matter. That is the norm. One of the many lines drawn for her kind which they must learn to live behind.

Jayanti was kind enough to cross those lines tonight. She had set out two cups and saucers on the tray. Bindiya had felt grateful for that rare gesture of parity. But then she cleared her throat, got Jayanti's attention, and pointed at the steel glasses in a corner.

A steel glass, wrapped in the saree's pallu to trap the warmth in for longer, encased in one's palms. Held close to the nose so the aroma reaches inside first and sets the stage. Lips, seared by hot metal at first contact, soothed by running the tongue freshly sweetened by sugar over them. That is how Bindiya liked her tea. Touch, smell, taste; an amalgamation of all the senses. Not the whole 'tea-in-a cup-placed-on-a-saucer-held-at-an-elbow's-distance' kind of thing. Such detachment. Such wastefulness. Living life one sensory fulfillment at a time. An act meant only for those who have a plenitude of everything. Bindiya and her kind must use everything to its fullest potential, and then squeeze harder for some more. That is how even a simple act of drinking tea turns into an art form. Old bedsheets become doors. Cement blocks become hammers. Ironing tables become...

"What if they call the Police?" Jayanti implores. Her cup is lingering mid-sip; her eyes are locked on the balconies.

Bindiya takes a long, noisy slurp. Its sound bounces off the silence and eases the night.

"They didn't when you call... so many time."

"But...", Jayanti gestures at the fire.

Bindiya holds the answer on her tongue for a bit, with a sip of tea. The umami of good quality cow's milk; a luxury she can discern without ever having tasted it before.

"If Police come... they can help us clean up ash!"

Tea comes flying out of Jayanti's mouth, on the wings of a chuckle, in a spray of brown mist now speckled on her saree's beige canvas. Sheer lightness follows. She realizes that she can do things like these now. He is not here to belittle her. For being human. For being her.

The evil in some people is so unexceptional that they are considered almost borderline good. And that makes it the perfect disguise. Besides, to the world, splinters under your skin – even a thousand of them – are hardly considered a wound. *What do you not have? Food? Good clothes? A roof over your head? What more does a husband owe a barren woman?* That is what they all said. That is what rotten wood said often too, while giving her countless splinters over the years. But rotten wood also burns faster; she reminds herself, as she looks at the fire starting to fold in on itself. Just over four hours. The human body usually takes about eight to ten. A silver lining, wherever she can find one.

The wind rustles, sweeping a few stray leaves into the fire. They burn on entry, flickering like fireflies. There is an odd beauty to this moment for those who know enough of the story to look for it. A melody Jayanti hasn't thought of in decades rises inside her. She wonders how her neighbors would react to her singing out loudly; here, at this moment. Will they fling their phones out and start recording again? That video will make the news for sure.

People are bored of the news of illness and death. Statistics now, all of them; numbers running in a steady ticker at the bottom of the TV screens. On the main screen, they want to see people consumed by downright insanity. Jayanti is reminded of what she saw on the news a few days ago; a woman trying to breathe into her husband's mouth to keep him alive, while his body lay splayed in the back seat of an auto-rickshaw. There were no beds left in the hospital. The corridors too were rammed full of the dead and the dying. The woman and her husband remained in that auto-rickshaw all day, parked right outside the hospital gate. Reporters had the opportunity to capture hours of footage. Of him, gasping for life. Of her, breathing all of hers into him. Reporters jostled about for hours, trying to get the perfect sound bite. *What do you think of the healthcare system in this country? How long have you been trying to get help? What do you have to say to the Government? Do you believe this virus was made in a lab?* The woman did her best to answer each one of them amidst her sobs; nobody acquiesces like the truly desperate. Suffixing each of her answers with a plea for help, hoping they will bring forth a miracle. They didn't. All of it made for sensational TV, though. Her husband's last breath was viewed live by millions of people all over the country.

Jayanti's video would provide a nice contrast to that woman's story, wouldn't it? She can practically visualize the caption on the screen.

Breaking News: Crazy woman sings next to her husband's funeral pyre in a communal park.

* * *

The fever had come five days ago, with that signature gut-tearing cough. Neighbors were quick to ostracise them, as is the norm these days. The second day he had gotten worse. Jayanti had run out to the edge of the park and called out for Bindiya. Requested her to grab some medicines. A young neighbor – replete with tattoos, piercings, and that signature apathy which youth brings – had voiced her disapproval, while watering her marigolds.

"Tch Tch... Order online, no! FoodPanda delivers everything now."

Jayanti had no energy to explain to the twenty-something that the world of sixty-somethings spins quite differently. On the generosity of neighbors. Or in the absence thereof, the neighborhood laundry lady.

By the fourth day, Jayanti's husband could hardly breathe. She had called every hospital in the city. Then the next city, though she had no idea how she would get there. She never had to find out.

"Could you send an ambulance..."

"All busy."

"Oxygen cylinder? I can pay double..."

"Not available."

Jayanti had done everything she could think of. Boiled and rubbed all kinds of herbs. All the balms and oils she could find. Months of medical wisdom received on WhatsApp, social media forwards, and neighborhood chatter were tried. None of them worked.

When his raucous coughing finally fell silent last night, Jayanti simply stood by the bed, wondering what else she could have done. Because those are the conjectures people will throw at her for the rest of her life. Things she could have done; should have done. Some might even suggest this is her fault, after all. If only she could bear children she wouldn't have been left alone to fend for herself today.

134

She had stood there till the pins and needles in her arms made her realize she had been pressing her palms against her mouth the entire time; her face frozen in a silent scream. She had run out of the house, barefoot. Rang doorbells. Rattled neighbors' iron gates. No one came. They displayed measured shock from the stipulated six feet away. Offered excuses from the balconies. Commiserated from behind their facemasks.

Jayanti had somewhat expected it, though. Rotten wood gives splinters to everyone. There wasn't a single family in the whole colony her husband hadn't managed to upset in some way or the other. Besides, her neighbors must have been hearing her screams all these years. Seen the bruises, when she stepped out to get milk from the milkman. They didn't come then. Why would they now?

She had then gone back inside and kept trying for an ambulance. Then the Police. And then, every single funeral home she could find in the number in the Yellow Pages. Most of them didn't even pick up. The ones that did, told her the waiting period in the crematorium was at least 48 hours.

"Twelve, if you have a letter from an MP," one of them had suggested kindly.

Where would a woman like Jayanti get a letter from a politician to prioritise her husband's cremation over the hundreds who must have died in this city today? It's not like it was something she could ask Bindiya to run out and grab for her.

Bindiya!

Jayanti had run out of the door yelling that name. She had barely made it to the end of the patio though, when, in the melting violet of the early morning, she noticed a body unfold and stand up next to the driveway gates. Bindiya had been sitting there, this whole time, waiting to be pressed into service.

*

The same Bindiya is now sitting next to Jayanti masticating a Marie biscuit, duly softened by dipping it in tea.

One look at Bindiya and Jayanti's shoulders relax. There is something about Bindiya – the way she is sitting, the way she is holding that steel glass, the way that limp Marie biscuit has all her attention. It seems like the world could end right now and Bindiya wouldn't care.

"It's over," Jayanti says to herself. Softly. Slowly. Stressing on every word. Lining it with faith.

The night continues to reward them with a breeze the fire could use. The two women continue to watch it and drink their tea.

"Did he beat you because no children?"

135

Jayanti's silhouette splits from Bindiya's. Shocked. By how blasé Bindiya's question is. By how accurate her assumption is. But what went on inside Jayanti's house was a secret to no one. Neither the neighbors nor the laundry woman. Jayanti exhales heavily and leans back comfortably on the bench. It feels peaceful. And deliciously comfortable. This night, this bench, some tea, and some truths finally laid bare.

"Pintu beat me too. Make them feel like man."

Some statements conclude a discussion before it has even begun. Jayanti feels grateful for this young woman's wisdom. For her presence. Without Bindiya there wouldn't have been this pyre. Only a festering body lying in Jayanti's bedroom. Only a name on a 48-hour waitlist for cremation.

It was Bindiya's idea.

It had been almost twenty hours. Even with the air conditioning, the body had started to stink. There was nowhere to go. No one was going to come to help. Bindiya's suggestion – as preposterous as it had sounded when she first made it – was the only option.

Besides, is this truly the most outrageous thing to have happened to a dead body this year, Jayanti wonders. Far more horrendous things are happening all over the world. In her country, even worse.

Even if people manage to take their dead to funeral homes, the wait times are appalling. That too for a bulk pyre, because one pyre per person is too slow to keep up. Wood is running low too. As are people who can dig the graves. Looking for a better option some people go to the river banks, bury the bodies in the sand, and leave. There are more sick to tend to back at home. But the sand graves are easy for the vultures to dig out and feast on. People who see the vultures swarming the bodies submit the bodies of their dearly departed into the rivers. A better goodbye; they assume. But the rivers spit the bodies out on the banks a few miles down where the dogs find them. Pictures of these horrific sights have made it to the covers of a few international magazines. What none of this makes for, though, is a dignified funeral. There are no dignified funerals in this pandemic. These are the times of doing what one needs to, to stay afloat. Countries are shutting their borders on their citizens stuck outside to protect the ones inside. People are stockpiling oxygen cylinders and lying to their dying relatives about having any. Lifesaving drugs are being black-marketed; parents are prioritizing the life of one child over another because medicine for one is all they can afford. Dead are being left unclaimed in the hospital morgues because their families don't know what else to do.

What is happening to Jayanti's husband is far better. It is far more than what Jayanti owes him.

*   *   *

Once the decision was made, everything happened rather quickly. Bindiya had grabbed what little coal she had left. Last year had been slow for business. Who needs ironed trousers during a pandemic? It would be enough to get the fire started, she had reckoned. This was her expertise, after all; making long-lasting fires in her box iron with the little coal she could afford to buy after her husband spent all their earnings on alcohol. She had scrambled some branches and twigs. Jayanti had brought out two old chairs. A large stash of old newspapers. Magazines. Two bottles of mustard oil, half a can of Canola. Jayanti had laid it all next to Bindiya's feet; offerings to the Goddess of Fire. Bindiya had gotten busy building a fire; while Jayanti had stood there watching her, distractedly scraping the dry ground with her feet until a sharp stone stung her big toe. A trickle of blood had sprung out. She had felt it before she saw it; wet and cold.

This was real. It was happening.

Jayanti was going to cremate her husband of thirty years, in the center of the Residents' Park of her colony, on a pyre made of an ironing table, broken chairs, leftover coal, old newspapers, and mustard oil, with only the colony's laundry lady by her side.

"Did you ever want kids?" Jayanti asks, shaking off any last shards of guilt.

"Naah. On the nights it rain, we sleep on table. Table not enough for even Pintu and me. Where kids sleep? Also, kids need all things... clothes, food, school dress... Na. Na. Na. The two times I got baby, I go to doctor. You know, that one. He give me tablet. Two days, all clean inside. Never told Pintu."

Jayanti's grip tightens around the armrest. The pumice-y surface of the bench digs into where the splinter is still lodged. Jayanti has paid the price for a sin she did not even commit, all her life. Enough doctors had ruled her out as the one with the problem. But who cares about such technicalities? If a child is missing from a marriage, the wife must pay for it. Jayanti did. In all possible currencies; slaps across the face, head slammed into walls, public ridicule, social ostracisation. And here is Bindiya, with her determined nonchalance about the matter.

"Then... Pintu died. So how have kids?" Bindiya takes one final loud slurp from her steel glass and puts it back on the tray.

Ten years ago, Bindiya's husband had consumed some adulterated liquor and died, right by their hut. People out on their morning walks had walked right past him. It was only a few hours later when Bindiya had returned after collecting the weekend's ironing from all the houses, that she realized what had happened. Thankfully the ironed clothes weren't needed until Monday morning so none of the residents had made a big fuss. One Mr. Randhawa had even been nice enough to call a pro-bono ambulance to take the body. Although, he also was the subject of the first set of rumors about the midnight park bench incidents. Jayanti can see how poorly children would have fitted into the milieu of Bindiya's life. The knot in her chest melts away. Bindiya – the young, illiterate laundry lady – understands things that sixty-year-old university-educated Jayanti doesn't. Jayanti is now a disciple, in the presence of the fount of wisdom. She thirsts for more.

"Why didn't you go back to your village, then... after Pintu died?"

"What for?" Bindiya releases her knee from her arm's hug and puts her leg down. She stretches both legs with relish, crosses them at the ankles, and starts to gently swing her sinewy toes. Jayanti notices the soles of Bindiya's feet. Calloused, cracked, but rugged. Years of standing next to the ironing table all day long have hardened her soles. Made her skin impenetrable. Her feet may not be pretty, but this woman can walk on fire now. Jayanti looks at her own feet. Bruised and bleeding from a single day's assault. She has a long way to go.

"He died. I didn't. This my home. Why go back?"

By the time Pintu had died, the makeshift supports of their hut had been replaced by two relatively stable walls. The thatched roof was a corrugated tin sheet. Instead of ironing on a thick mat on the floor, they had a table. Five feet by three. Long enough to iron sarees and bedsheets; which meant more income. Theirs had become a decent operation, or at the very least more functional. Steady business from the whole of the colony followed. They could afford to eat twice a day; even afford some fish every once in a while. Bindiya had nested, in whatever limited way that term could be applied to her life. And none of that had changed with Pintu's death. Bindiya was right. She really had no reason to leave all this and go back.

Jayanti had tried to leave many times. That time when he had locked her in the kitchen for hours because the food was a little too salty. When he had almost broken her arm. The many nights he had raped her violently. Her parents always discouraged her; they were too old to deal with all this. Her brothers had their own families to worry about. Her friends had told her she was overreacting. That men are hot-headed. These things happen.

Jayanti realizes her mistake now. She asked others for permission. Bindiya never does.

The women continue sitting under the moonless sky. The world around them gradually heads inside. Tired, finally. Or stymied, perhaps; by the magnitude of what these women have managed to do without their help. Without their permission.

Jayanti notices the flames getting shorter and erratic. The window is small. A gear shifts. She gets up, gestures to Bindiya to follow her, walks up to Bindiya's hut, and stops.

"Grab what you must. Rest, I will buy for you."

Bindiya balks. But something in Jayanti's voice – a steely tone mixed with peace – which Bindiya has never heard before makes her snap into action. She walks inside her hut, starts to ruffle through her stuff, picks up a thing or two almost ceremonially, and reaches for the box iron.

"You won't need that anymore."

Bindiya gives one long look to Jayanti, then to the box iron, and then to Jayanti, again. Finally, Bindiya smiles and walks out of the hut. She is almost at the end of the park when a thought makes her swing back. She comes back holding a block of cement. Her face is a picture of contentment.

The two women go inside Jayanti's house. Jayanti points to the room where Bindiya can put her things. When Bindiya is done she finds Jayanti standing in her bedroom, staring at the bed. It stinks. Jayanti grabs one end of the mattress. Bindiya instinctively grabs the other.

They drag it to the center of the park and throw it in the fire. The cotton ignites on contact. They behold the exuberant flames for a while and then go back inside. Thirty years leave a lot behind to purge. Jayanti collects it all and hands it to Bindiya, who then runs out and throws them into the fire. Clothes, belts, towels, pillows, blankets, shoes, cigarettes. His presence is being erased in the same fire he is. After what feels like the last run, Bindiya waits by the fire. Jayanti takes a while to come.

"Do you think these will burn?" Bindiya turns around to find Jayanti standing by the fire, with a bag heaving with cups and saucers. Dozens of them.

Bindiya shrugs, takes the bag from Jayanti, and starts throwing the cups and the saucers into the fire. Jayanti smiles and joins her; the two of them tossing cups and saucers into the fire, like children skipping rocks on a lake.

Jayanti casts the last cup and whispers to Bindiya, "Teach me how to drink tea in a steel glass."

The Invented Languages of Adela Arkani

1: Photo-Sensitive Language

Public bathrooms, if used correctly, had the prophetic powers of a fortune telling toy I had as a kid, the Magic 8 Ball. I could ask any question aloud in bathrooms and wait for the random responses of people in the other stalls, who were each struggling with their own difficulties, to provide an answer. "What did my son, Xavi, think when I didn't support him after his daughter was born?" I asked aloud, running my hands through my white beard.

"This stinks," someone shouted from one stall.

"Was I a bad or good father to Xavi?" I asked.

"Number 2!" Someone else shouted. Maybe that random stranger was correct. I'd made the right choice to show Xavi tough love by refusing to give him money until he started working and taking care of his daughter more. I exited the bathroom. The first stars were starting to disappear from the pre-dawn sky. Time was running out before Xavi's daughter, Adela, and I had to go to work.

"Wild ride in there, huh grandpa?" Adela asked.

"I'm okay," I said. The drug that made my language sensitive to light had been upsetting my stomach. "Let's go grab some herbs that might settle my stomach from the garden," I said.

"I know drugs work more than my dad," Adela said as we walked to the workers' garden. "But how do they work?" I didn't know how to answer without depressing her. She was soon going to be old enough to have to take the drugs, too.

"My speech dims as it grows brighter outside," I said. "Each morning, I stop speaking as the sun rises above the strawberry fields of Pajaro Dunes, California," I explained, waving my hands over the still-dark horizon.

"What's it like to stop speaking once it's bright out?" she asked. I thought of pleasure. When enough pleasure shone through me, thinking ceased and all that was left was feeling. Anxiety could have the same effect, leaving me able to feel only tension and think of nothing else. It was too hard to explain all that to her. Instead, I said, "I think it's like being a dog. You can understand a few words, but you're not computing anything through linguistic thought." Our dog, Haunts, followed Adela around the garden and gave me a look.

"Do you like not speaking because it means you stop arguing with my Dad?" She was young enough that my disappointment in her father, Xavi, could appear like playing pretend. But she was old enough that the clarity of her questions could be measured by the heartache in my answers.

"Yes," I had to admit. When Adela was born, she looked just like the stranger Xavi was to me when he was a newborn. I used to think that the move from being a stranger to a loved one in a relationship was like the shift from proficiency to fluency in a language. But it was the opposite. Relationships, after enough time, required the work of a non-fluent speaker. I had to express myself through what was not easy or did not feel natural.

"It's not his fault that he's raising me on his own," Adela said.

"Yes it is," I said.

"I'll talk to him," she said. Bickering, to her, was the engine of adult relationships. And eleven years of watching us bicker had made her believe that if she could sound grown-up, or at least make her language more complex, then maybe she could talk to Xavi in a way that would snap him out of his depression that started when Adela's mom left him shortly after she was born.

"You' don't have to do that. I'll talk to him," I said. I hadn't accepted Xavi's choices. I didn't like that he had a kid so young. Maybe I'd made a mistake. Regret was clarity about the choices I'd made. Heartache was clarity about the choices I no longer had. I needed language to process regret. But heartache seemed to be a languageless emotion immune to the drugs we were on.

"Can anything resist the effect of the drugs?" Adela asked.

"Maybe a good argument," I said. I fantasized about good arguments more than I fantasized about great sex. 45 years of religious upbringing made it hard for me to fantasize about pleasure. And since something like fantasy could impede pleasure, I wondered if there was a structure of thinking that might also resist the drug. "Arguments with your grandma Dori didn't stop after we started taking the drugs," I added. Adela's grandma, Dori, had died from too much fluid in her lungs. Her overworked heart caused an increase in blood pressure, and that pushed blood into the air sacs in her lungs. She drowned in her own body. This drowning occurred so shortly before Adela was born that it was as though Dori had disappeared beneath a sea, tried coming back up for air, and came up as Adela instead.

Morning twilight was starting to brighten our garden where we grew artichokes, sunflowers, and snap peas. It was also starting to reveal the stains of Modelo that had spilled on my white t-shirt the night before. Unlike jeans and male egos, society did not ascribe more value to t-shirts the more they were distressed. I hid the stains by turning from Adela in the garden to button my long-sleeve shirt. I faced the workers' cabin nearby and its little window with a checkered blue-and-white curtain. I had only a few minutes of language left until the sun erased my ability to think for the rest of the day. The window curtain had spent its life learning to dance from the way that Xavi used to play outside it as a child, and then how he slow-danced in the garden with Adela. "You've got no rhythm," I said to the curtain through the window, and it turned its back on me in the wind. As a parent, maybe the light in my eyes, like twilight, was too weak and diffused for Xavi to have ever seen much in it. At best, he might have once felt a kind of sleepy wonder beneath my gaze. Wild weeds grew in our garden easily. But in my life, it was the opposite. The truly wild parts of life took the most effort to guard and maintain, like the memory of my Xavi when he was a child and we were close. "Is that how my child danced?" I had to ask my window curtain now that I could not remember.

Xavi woke up and shuffled towards the garden in his Crocs to have his morning smoke. "Say Rest in Peace to your Grandpa," he said to Adela and made the sign of the cross.

"Stop rehearsing for my funeral with her," I said.

Xavi asked me, "What's something that won't come at the right time and that a handful of people will try hard not to laugh at?"

"My funeral?" I responded.

"That's one answer," Xavi said. "But I don't know if you'll ever die, old man," he said. The only thing Xavi liked more than hip hop were folkoric cryptid monsters like the Fresno Nightwalkers, the Chupacabra, and near-immortal beings like vampires and angry fathers.

Xavi dropped his cigarette and stomped it out in the soil. It was his time to play act as a dad to Adela. Each morning, they took at least a few minutes to play before Adela went to work with me. They started playing a hand-clapping game, with our dog Haunts curled up by their feet. *Hello operator, Please give me number nine. And if you disconnect me, I'll chop of your...Behind the frigerator...* I watched them and tried to say something. But not speaking seemed more important. The artichokes that we grew for ourselves in the workers' garden had taste inhibitors that hid some of their bitterness and made them taste a touch sweeter. Their small bit of sweetness came not from what was added to the tongue, but from what was subtracted. It was the last thought that I had before the bosses whistled and the sun's first rays above California's coastal range signaled it was time to work.

2: Proprioception Based Language

"What should I say to Xavi?" I asked the ghost of Adela's deceased grandmother, Dori, in the bathroom the next morning.

"Something hurts," someone else responded from another stall. Maybe that was the key. I needed to let Xavi know how I was feeling but leave just enough detail out to pique his curiosity. Dori had always cooked us meals using fresh ingredients from the garden. But, like chefs in many families, she left out an ingredient or two from the recipe so that, if someone was really interested in knowing how to make things right, they'd have to ask her personally to tell them more. Gardens could teach me about absence as much as they could teach me about abundance.

"Hey, Xavi," I said to him in the garden that morning.

"Not now," he said. He wasn't wearing his Crocs. He had on running shoes. Instead of a cigarette, he was holding one of Adela's hands.

Each morning, Xavi and Adela had been practicing new hand-clapping routines. At first, this charade of being a real dad didn't last much longer than the smoke hanging in the air after he finished his cigarette. But Adela kept coaxing him out. She believed that if she could get him to learn new ways of playing and speaking to her, then they might develop the language they needed to connect. Against my pessimistic predictions, she was right. They had kept playing each morning and, after a while, they didn't need to use words at all. They communicated almost everything they needed through their hands. They'd formed their own private language.

To show how he was a great dad who didn't need my advice, Xavi explained how this marvelous language worked. As he droned on, I noticed Adela drawing in her notebook in the garden. She was drawing little boys' butts in various positions all next to one another, with a much bigger butt in the middle presiding over the dinner table the butts had gathered around. It looked like the famous painting of The Last Supper, except the stern, but forgiving Lord at the center was substituted for singular set of muscular, but huggable glutes surrounded by attentive disciples. She had talent. Each butt seemed to be staring back at her with an irresistible prejudice in her favor, understanding her just as far as she wanted to be understood.

Xavi stretched his "hammies" and then launched into how his new way of speaking to his daughter worked. To conjugate a verb, one person would clap slightly before the other to indicate the past. They clapped simultaneously to indicate the present. Or one would clap slightly after to indicate the future. But because anything could be percussive on the body—fingers snapping, feet stomping, or chests bumping and so on— they could combine these percussive sounds to create more verb tenses than an English or Spanish speaker could imagine. They lived in a different sense of time. Each noun was a combination of many things: the vertical and horizontal positions of their hands when they clapped and the shape of their fingers or hands between claps. In the same way that they started showing their love to one another through the repetition of caring more for each other each day, some of their nouns also required the repetition of several of the same motions. When a sign language developed in an organic way like this, it was often called a "home sign." Their home sign required two people to generate each sentence. Given the extra person and extra set of hands, each sentence could convey more information than any one person could do so alone.

I gleaned other information from observing them. The complexity of their emotional responses grew in proportion to the complexity of their language. Xavi could be agitated while Adela was making signs that I knew to be associated with saying 'Thank you.' Some information was visual onomatopoeia. The phrase 'cute, little butt,' for example, involved exactly what Adela appeared to want to do each time she saw one, which was a grabbing and slapping motion.

The language spread. More children learned it. I tried to learn but was too old. My neurons associated with language had been dimmed by the drug. Those neurons were down a dark cerebral hallway from neurons that remained unaffected and continued lighting up with activity. I could feel something like a glimmer of thought when the language related neurons were briefly illuminated by the faraway light of the neurons that were still functioning. Even during the dark hours, when language was supposed to be easiest for me, taking this drug for the past couple years had spillover effects. I'd been almost entirely languageless from morning twilight to evening starlight, and now was starting to feel similar effects even at night.

Before long, the bosses said, "These are for Adela." She had aged into the requirement to take the drugs in order for her to retain her citizenship. I handed over the $10 I had to pay each day for the bosses to drive us from the workers' cabin to the fields only a half mile away, and then I grabbed our pills.

I wondered whether I'd speak to Adela about her need to start taking the pills in English or Spanish. My mother tongue was Spanish. I was fluent in English, but it had taken me a long time to feel at home in that language. I didn't feel like a native speaker in English until I'd given my own father's eulogy in English. To me, a language was like a country in the sense that I didn't feel like I belonged there until I had buried someone in it.

The bosses on the farm had said no one could resist the drug. And, each morning, they'd seemed right. After we loaded up in company vans, and the sun started pouring through the window, we lost our ability to speak or keep track of time as the sun rose and then fully beat down on us. We usually earned piece-rate. But if we worked over a certain number of hours, then California required that the bosses pay us overtime. We didn't realize when we worked past the hour when overtime pay should have started.

That all seemingly changed the day that Adela started working while on the drug. I was working in one part of the field where the coastal fog was obscuring the sun. My language started coming back as the fog dimmed the light. I stared at my hands and thought about all the things that they had held without me thinking about them—my son, Xavi, included. I looked up and felt the dizzying sensation of being able to think during daylight hours. The moving bodies of workers glittered across the fields in a colorful array of clothing to protect their skin from the sun. Without knowing it, we had been bestowing on the real a richness that we were told was missing from our own imaginations. In the distance, I saw Adela. She was in a part of the field flooded by sunlight. A mirage, shimmering in the distance, made it look as though the air was daydreaming. Adela and her friends should have been languageless because of the light. But they were speaking with their hands, asking each other for help when they needed it. They were making the work less tiring by helping each other out. They worked piece-rate, so they limited their speaking to keep their hands free as much as they could. But they'd found a language resistant to the drug that they could use when needed. The irony wasn't lost on me that the only language that functioned was one that slightly slowed down their pace of work, but that was better than nothing at all.

My relationship with Xavi softened. Some mornings, on the edge of darkness and twilight, we walked to the bluffs overlooking the Pacific Ocean while he fought the urge to smoke. The wind's face appeared in the ripples stretching across the sea below us. We used to be so close when he was a boy. Embraces from him used to be like those ripples across the sea. They showed the contours of something that was otherwise invisible between us. But I couldn't remember the last time we'd embraced. Instead of putting his arm around my shoulders, he just asked, "You hear that new J-Cole album?"

3. Absence based language

Soon, the bosses caught on. They gave us stronger drugs. They suppressed the new language. We feared they'd give us drugs that would make our language sensitive to other things ranging from the frivolous to the powerful, Golden Retrievers to the Holy Cross. People weren't making as much money as they used to and some families, even though they worked on the farm, were going hungry. To someone like me whose faith was wavering, the ribs that appeared on hungry bodies functioned like breath appearing on a mirror I imagined placing by the lips of the country's dominant idea of a Christian God to confirm if He was still alive. Each rib that showed through someone's skin was proof that He was and that I might no longer be able to pray.

Adela got quiet and didn't speak, even at night. Xavi stopped playing with her in the mornings. It took me awhile, but I got the idea to order a taxi to take us to her favorite restaurant by the beach to cheer her up. Near the beach was a Popeyes with dimmed light made especially for workers like us. Enough workers had been on the drugs long enough that some businesses had caught-on and changed to attract more clientele. Popeyes was the name of where we ate and also the expression on our faces in the bathroom after eating there. I used the bathroom while Xavi and Adela waited outside. Flecks of toilet paper that were stained red and brown circled around my feet like a Koi Pond. When I left the bathroom, I saw an expression that was newer for Xavi's face: concern.

"What happened?" I asked.

"Some kids pranked us. They turned the lights on. We all got disoriented. I don't know where Adela ran off to," he said. "She's lost."

"If she gets too far, the streetlights will make it too hard for us to think or find her," I said.

"I know. Help me," Xavi said. I think he was able to ask me for help again because, by wanting the same thing, we had one less veil of privacy between us. We both wanted Adela back and feared losing her. Loss was to privacy what time was to cooking. It helped us know when to share what we'd covered or contained.

I was scared that Adela might be shrieking in horror at being lost. We were in a section of the boardwalk with businesses that had dimmed their lights to attract customers like us. But other stores had brightly-lit windows strong enough to disorient Adela. The closer we got to those other stores, the more that other people's children were running around us laughing and shouting to their friends. The crowds on the sidewalk were likely mistaking her cries of terror for cries of delight. To live in this country was to be in a place where so many screams could be misheard as joy. I felt a tightness in my chest and couldn't breathe well. Wondering whether I'd lost Adela momentarily or for forever, my anxiety began operating on loss the way that grammar operated on verb tenses in a language. Anxiety was conjugating loss, making me hear how the present situation could continue far into an imperfect future.

We left the boardwalk for the darkness of the beach, hoping to find her there. Xavi and I walked closely together. The further we got from the city lights, the sharper our language became.

"This is your fault," Xavi said.

"What?" I asked. I was stunned. He was the one watching her when she ran off. This was his fault.

"This was all your idea," he said.

Instead of arguing with him, I asked, "Why is it so hard for us to talk?"

"You tell me," Xavi said. I searched my brain for anything that might connect us.

"Maybe English and Spanish were languages that, since their very beginning, were meant to be as detrimental as the drugs we took," I said. "Maybe they are languages that have been designed from the start to muddy our thinking."

"Oh, like a linguistic version of Bigfoot? Something that keeps itself, or at least the thoughts that occur in it, perpetually out of focus?"

"Sure," I said, "if you need to think of it that way."

"You can't use your difficulties with language as an excuse for never telling me what I needed to hear," Xavi said. Before I could say more, Xavi spotted Adela by the waves and ran towards her.

"Why did you run off on us like that?" I asked Adela. She didn't respond. She'd gotten lost and disoriented and I'd blamed her.

"I'm so happy we found you," Xavi said, and she turned at that and gave him a hug.

"Designing a new language?" I asked. Adela had been skipping rocks that sank into the water and was throwing sand into the air that disappeared with the wind. It looked like she was testing a new language that used the sounds that small, ordinary objects make when they leave the familiar world behind. Instead of answering me, she bent down and made two little mounds in the sand. A butt. Classic Adela.

"What you been thinking about out here?" Xavi asked Adela before she could answer me.

"A lot," she said.

"Tell me what's up," he said. They walked a few steps ahead of me on the beach further away from the city lights. I tried listening to their conversation, but I couldn't hear them any better than I could hear Dori. The wind had shifted away from Xavi and Adela offshore, towards where it was the darkest.

SHANE TIVENAN

Mother versus Deep Blue

opening

Rudolf Spielmann said the beauty of a game of chess can only be assessed by the sacrifices it contains (The Art of the Sacrifice, 1935). Mother read Spielmann as a child. She taught me the game aged 3. It'll help you make better decisions, she said. It'll make you more creative.

Once mother stopped finding joy in the mere playing of chess, she began to paint. She started simple. She drew main lines taken from classic bouts, and slowly superimposed layers of colour for emotions that arise during games. White for the waiting move, the passive play. Blue for calm intellect. Purple for the psychology, the mind trickery. Red for sacrifice. Black for the paranoia. Her muse from the start was Kasparov.

It was Kasparov's genius that inspired mother towards the chess artist she became. It was the aesthetic of how he went about his business. His head-holding pose as he tried vice-grip the right move from his mind. The patterns that appeared on his side of the board to signal to his opponent what was coming. The Sicilian Nadjorf. The Scotch Game. The Gruenfeld, exchange variation. The Petrov Defense. And what Kasparov sought and what mother wanted to capture was the unique positional pattern a brilliancy could make. A thing brand new put on display upon its conception, so beautiful and destructive that it could end his opponents game on the spot. End careers. Inflict psychological damage. Crown Kasparov as world champion.

Art must always make a connection son, Mother said to 16-year-old me in 1996 after the news came in that Kasparov had won his first match against IBM's Deep Blue. Mother sketching as she spoke.

Connection, I said. Cool.

Within art there has to be something for people to feel. To recognise.

Ok.

I tell my canvasses everything, you know that don't you? That's the sacrifice we make.

I didn't respond. She had lost me by this stage.

*   *   *

149

The work Mother did on Kasparov brought her great success as a visual artist, enough that she could leave her office job as an accountant during her 40s and focus solely on her art. From the latter half of the 80s through the guts of the 90s, mother landscaped abstract worlds based on chess games, and Kasparov's sharp lines provided the cartographic nodes. Her boarded worlds always rose up in the centre, showing the importance of the central squares. Showing the constant power struggle between two people, she began to say in later years, once the arguments had begun.

Her triptych on the first world championship match between Kasparov and Karpov, 1985, Moscow, was the work that got her shortlisted for the Turner Prize. Game 16 from that match went down as one of Kasparov's immortals. With the black pieces, he managed to outpost a heavily protected knight deep into Karpovian territory. An earlier pawn sacrifice allowed him to do this, a carbon copy of a move he had attempted in game 12. Karpov, having accepted the poisoned sacrifice, advanced his C and E pawns and was left with no protectors to kick away the knight that now controlled the whole board. For the following 18 moves, this piece controlled the whole world of chess. Its domination kept white's rooks out of the game and left one of Karpov's own knights stranded out in no-mans-land on A4.

That is what a brilliancy is, mother explained to me as she stood back and tilted her head up at the giant snapshot of the game postered to her studio wall as she worked on the pieces in the late 1980s. That is complete intellectual strangulation, she said, and I could not tell if she was happy or sad as she shook her head and looked up at the wall, her face the face of someone idolising a fresco or a picture of a child.

By the time Kasparov played knight to D3 in match 16, move 16, Karpov was already in *zugzwang* – a nightmare situation in chess where even though it is your turn, any move is detrimental to your position. On move 34, Karpov was forced to sacrifice his queen just to remove the knight, but he did it too late. The losing position he never recovered from, not in the game nor in the match overall. Kasparov took the title of world champion from Karpov, at just 22 years old, 1985, still the youngest ever to do so. He would remain world champion for 15 years, and would retain his world number one status for the rest of his professional career.

At his peak, Kasparov was invincible. Mother's interpretation of game 16 in Moscow, entitled *Octopus Knight,* was the one that got her shortlisted for the 1989 Turner Prize. A welcome shock for us all. But that mother was artsy was shock in itself. Daughter of farmers. Married to another accountant. No creative flair as a child. The only problem for mother and I was that my father did not take to her new lifestyle, to her new found fame.

It's the important work, I heard her saying to him when he quizzed her decision to leave the stability of her 9 to 5. Creativity is the only true work for me at the moment, she said.

And money is the only true language for me, he said back, and for bank managers and mortgage brokers. Look, you're no Picasso darlin', you're an accountant – an accounting technician before you met me, I might add.

I'll bring in my share still, she said, the work is starting to pay off.

Eavesdropping on their conversation, I remember feeling it so cold how they spoke to each other. Like they weren't married but in business together, and the business didn't seem to be going great. My father always playing the angry old boss, but mother held. She painted. She brought home good money and father got lost in his own work, was home less and less to have dinner with us in the evening.

* * *

In the run up to Kasparov's rematch with Deep Blue in New York, the headline touted at the time was *The Brain's last Stand* (Newsweek, May 3rd, 1997). Kasparov went into a 12 month period of grief after that match. When the dust settled, years later, he explained that yes, he had played computers before and since the Deep Blue rematch. He played Deep Blue's forefather, Deep Thought, in 1989 (Deep Thought 0 - 2 Kasparov). In 1996 he took out Deep Blue in their initial match behind closed doors. The Israeli Deep Junior held him to a draw in the early 90s (3-3). The German supercomputer, Fritz, the same in '03. But in New York, 1997, full house including mother and myself (me wearing a *the brain will not be bested* t-shirt and stoned on a blunt of weed I won off one of the chess hustlers in Washington State Park that morning), a giant board and notated moves projected onto a screen over the stage, and after each match Kasparov and the IBM team would come out and face the crowd and take media questions. The tension built and built as Kasparov, the hands-down favourite to begin with, took game 1, but by game 4 he had dropped to rank outsider as the world began to realise that this computer was now playing grandmaster level chess. Kasparov managed to scrape some draws and we met him with a standing ovation as he walked across the stage afterwards, the penny having dropped for all in attendance that we we were no longer just cheering Kasparov on, we were cheering on ourselves as possessors of biological brains and beating hearts and creative thinking minds which were trying to prove their worth against the machine. Mother squeezed my hand through all the tense periods of play during that match. Looking at me each time Kasparov

Shane Tivenan

found a way to protect himself, whispering in my ear, We have it son, we have it. He's going to find a brilliancy and win the match. Just watch. But after the final game her hand went limp and she did not look at the stage nor me. She just stared at the back of the seat in front of her. Months later, Kasparov himself would state that he was not just defeated by Deep Blue that day, he was killed.

Up until that point of our chess lives together, mother would always explain to me that the chess-playing style of a computer was brute force. It was a slow moving wall that closes in on its opponents and takes takes takes, capturing all available material. A computer does not understand sacrifice and it is blind to the dangers of accepting one, just as Karpov was in game 16, 1985, Moscow. A computer lacks hunch and instinct, and it can never play a psychological move. And Kasparov, he had prepared to play a computer. He was battle hardened for the brute force, but in game 2 towards the latter half of the middle game, he offered up a pair of pawns to Deep Blue, convinced the computer would take them which would allow holes to be punctured in Deep Blue's defence. But Deep Blue did not do what a computer is supposed to do. It thought hard. It crashed. It rebooted. Kasparov sweated and paced and held his head in the corner of the stage as after the third reboot, with fresh buffers and logs to think through, Deep Blue refused the sacrificial material, a sacrifice in itself, and it played instead a beautiful move. It played a human move.

When interviewed before the rematch in 1997, the IBM engineers took questions on their computer's preparation. The engineers played down speculation that Deep Blue was preparing specifically to play Kasparov. Deep Blue does not know it is playing Kasparov, they stated. Deep Blue does not even know it is playing chess.

But Mother would argue, Kasparov would argue, by game two, move 36, Deep Blue knew exactly what it was doing.

On our flight home from New York, I tried coaxing mother into playing a game of blitz on my travel-board, but she turned away, staring out the porthole. The beautiful game is dead, she said. She stopped painting in the latter half of that year. She returned to her office job as an accountant and her unused canvasses were stored in the attic.

middlegame

Prior to walking away from the art world, mother would pass afternoons watching top ranking chess players simultaneously compose and perform their work while she lined and coloured their moves. She figured out ways to snare Kasparov's sharp lines, his deviations, his traps. She captured his opponent's paranoia, and even Kasparov's own as he saw a weakness in one of his moves and left the board immediately after playing so as to distance his fear from his opponents, lest they seize on it. She painted players chasing ghosts, running from ghosts, as the paranoia in a game is sometimes enough to see threats that do not exist and to play overly defensive moves when no real attack is there. And Kasparov, he could play the ghost move, the psychological move, then sit back and stare his opponent down as if he himself were haunting them. For a piece entitled *Death by Bishop* (Oil on canvas, 72 X 56), mother slashed her canvas with a thousand diagonals from bottom right to top left, just as Kasparov had run a thousand fianchettoed bishops along the diagonal from G2 to B7. Exposing fatal attacks. Leaving his opponent's pieces hanging.

The Guardian's art critic, Gillian Small, said in her review of the Turner Prize's 1989 shortlist that mother had captured Kasparov's thought processes and transposed them onto canvas. Small went on to detail how this transposition took place. How mother traced Kasparov's moves but left a time-trail echo out behind to show each piece's complete path throughout a game. Each trail of moves layered upon the next and showing the incredible sharp openings, the pawn pushes, the marshalling rooks, and ending on the positional masterpieces which Kasparov dedicated his life to finding, mother's to drawing. By the end of a game, by the end of a painting, what emerged on mother's canvas was not some abstract mess that needed imagination and red wine to interpret, but real patterns of geometric beauty. This artist, said Small in her article, has managed to map the footprints of a mind. She has taken a snapshot of the subconscious to show what true creative decision making looks like, and laid it out for all to see on a 64 x 64 oil on canvas.

* * *

The Mechanical Turk (Wolfgang Von Kempelen, 1770) was a chess playing apparatus that travelled the world in the 18th century and won the majority of its games. It was automaton. A carnivalesque wooden box with a mechanical man making moves. His eyes even roaming about the board, as if thinking deeply. The Mechanical Turk was labelled as witchcraft. As demonic. As Godly. It travelled the world many times over, beating grandmasters and royalty. It smashed Napoleon Bonaparte in less than 20 moves and I have to think to myself, did Napoleon feel in 1802 what Kasparov felt in New York in 1997? Was he paranoid? Did he suspect something was amiss or did he truly believe that a machine was

153

this good at chess? But Napoleon and the chess world took a breath of relief when the writer Edgar Allen Poe revealed The Mechanical Turk to be a fraud (a real grandmaster hidden inside making all the moves), and after game two in New York, 1997, Kasparov decided the same thing was happening all over again – there was something inside Deep Blue pulling the levers. He wanted to go into the data server room and inspect Deep Blue. The IBM engineers said, Read the small print Garry, the data server room is out of bounds. Kasparov then demanded a printout of Deep Blue's logs. Why all the crashes? Why the restarts? Why the great move after such a restart? Read the small print Garry. But what Kasparov truly wanted was to smash Deep Blue's titanium skull open and walk in and look around with his flashlight and grandmaster detector device.

I wanted to do something similar to my father when he left us. I wanted to smash his head in and have a good look around inside. Find the ghost pulling the levers that controlled his hands to pack his suitcase and powered his legs to walk out the door. Find the mechanical voice box that made him say those words to mother as he did so.

The white for passive play, the waiting move, that's my father not coming home for dinner, I said to mother over the kitchen table in 1999, aged 20, slit-eye stoned and half drunk. Is it not?

No. Not consciously anyways. I've always said that I tell my canvasses everything son but that's not the way it works. I don't set out to express anything in particular, I just follow the flow as it comes.

You would have known at the time he was fucking about though would you not?

I had an idea, yes. And nice language by the way, I've reared you well.

And that would have come out in the work would it not?

It all comes out, yes.

Then why be so cryptic with me? You could have said that's what you were thinking all along.

You were a child back then, and by the looks of it you still are. You're just a drunk and stoned child now.

Purple for the psychological move - I can see that now. Him telling you that you drove him away with your obsession with art and chess. I heard him say that at Christmas. That you weren't there for him. Purple equals his mind trickery. Isn't it?

Calm down, son. We can't keep going over this.

Red for sacrifice, I said. Him sacrificing his family for his young accounting protégé. A very human move I feel. A pattern even. Did he not label you as his protégé before you married him? Did you not tell me that when I was a child?

She said nothing.
A nasty move, I said.

endgame

I flew mother to Washington last year to visit the National Museum of American History. Mother's senility meant she did not quiz me too much on why the big trip or why that museum. We landed in Washington at midday and we were in the museum by 2pm. I led her downstairs to the technology exhibition and I walked her over to the corner display:

Deep Blue (IBM RS/6000 SP2)

We stood in front of Deep Blue 25 years after it took out Kasparov. 24 years after father left us. 3 years after mother's senility had begun. Mother pushed her head again its titanium casing and I didn't try stop her. Her short term memory fading fast but she did not need an explanation as to what she was looking at. She knew Deep Blue, fingering the sign that told her it could calculate 200 million positions per second. Kasparov? Maybe two. She knew it was the same Deep Blue who could see hundreds of moves ahead at all times. Kasparov? 30. Max. And only at the beginning of a game when he was entering into a well trodden and prepped main line. After that, once middle game was reached, Kasparov could see only a handful of moves in front of him. In the endgame the same, unless it was a set mating net - a trap you could not escape. Mother pushed hard as she could against Deep Blue. Against its 1.5 tonne. Against its mind so large as to have been split between twin titanium 6ft 5 cabinets. Its left and right lobe. Kasparov? 5ft 9. 12 stone. A 1.3kg brain. Blood and bone he was, but mostly water.

How had he any hope against that monster, mother?

Mother stayed leaning in against the machine, saying nothing.

I looked at mother as we walked back upstairs. I looked at her tears. I thought about all the other art she could have produced over the last number of years if Deep Blue had not taken out her muse. I wished for the courage to go back downstairs and call out Deep Blue. I wished for a mind imbued with enough processing power for 201 million positional moves a second. For the ability to see 500 moves into the future.

Mother said she needed the bathroom and I waited close-by. I sat on an enormous bean bag and took out my phone and played a one minute game of bullet chess. I came out of the game and still no mother. Each time she

155

goes missing I fear the worst, even just around our house at home. It's only the two of us, and so if I go and do our weekly shop and come back and she's nowhere to be seen, my mind races. She has walked out onto the road. She slipped out the back and can't get up. She is alone somewhere, confused and scared. I found a female security guard on her rounds and asked her to go into the toilet to check on mother, explaining her condition. The security guard reappeared and explained mother was not in that toilet. She contacted her colleagues and instructed them to keep an eye out for someone fitting mother's description – she was not to be let leave the building on her own. We searched the floor we were on but mother was nowhere. The security guard asked where we had spent most of our time in the museum and I explained and we made our way to the stairs leading to the technology exhibition. Half way down, we met her being escorted up by two other security guards. Mother had plugged out Deep Blue.

She was smiling as they ushered us towards the museum Café where we were given complimentary tea and donuts. Not used to such acts coming from the elderly and senile, the security people asked her in monotone voices, Mam, are you ok? Would you like some water? Sit here mam, please. Relax. You are in a museum, do you know that mam? And I realised looking at them and listening to their words that they thought her act a mistake. They felt sorry for her. They thought she thought she was plugging out her television set before going upstairs to bed. They did not recognise it for what it was. An act of sabotage. A beautiful move. We ate their donuts and drank their tea.

* * *

Our flight home was delayed so we played chess in the departure lounge on my travel board, and mother can still play well. Every time she looks at the board she sees a brand new game, but the lines and positions from a thousand grandmaster clashes are embedded within her. We drank more tea. Mother played black and laid out a solid Sicilian. By move 15 she had me in a chess headlock. I looked out the window at the runways and lines of people coming and going and little tractors taxiing enormous planes to and from their docks. Mother asked an airport volunteer for a pen and began sketching on our napkins. Kasparov and Deep Blue chatting on a bench in Central Park. Deep Blue holding its arms up and Kasparov running a stethoscope over its chest, shaking his head. Deep Blue leaning in and resting on Kasparov's shoulder. Kasparov looking off into the distance, smiling to himself.

Your move, she said.

156

MARY WANG

The Child is a Mother Too

Now that she was expecting, the woman bought vitamins, tracking apps, and books that told her what to expect.

She fantasized about a wardrobe of stretchy dresses that would cradle her bump, a sling in which she could carry her baby to events. She started looking into the school district her apartment was zoned in.

We didn't come to America so you can send my grandchild to public school, her mother would've said.

She had no idea yet of all the things that could go wrong while bearing a new life, so, at six weeks, the woman informed her friends, some work contacts, and others she pictured she would invite to her baby shower. Her mother had just died—who else was she going to tell?

"You're keeping it?" A asked, as the woman announced the news to her friends at a Lower East Side gallery opening. They were standing in a cavernous space in which a Norwegian artist-duo was growing fungi in glass vitrines.

"I am," the woman replied. "Even though per New York standards, I'll basically be a teen mom."

She was twenty-nine.

"I never pictured you as a mother," B added, who was certain she wanted a PhD more than she wanted children.

The pregnancy wasn't planned, exactly. The woman told her boyfriend she had forgotten to take the pill, to which he responded with an ambiguous nod. A few weeks later, she started noticing the tenderness in her breasts and her sudden bouts of car sickness. She took a test, then another one. After a year filled with death and disappointment, the knowledge that something was growing inside her filled the woman with a welcome sense of achievement.

"I'm just looking forward to feeling that immense, self-sacrificial sense of purpose, you know?"

"Good for you," A said, who was coming out of a string of short-lived romances with straight men who didn't treat waiters nicely. "I'm jealous."

The woman turned her gaze away from her friends and looked at the Petri dishes secured behind the vitrines. She swore she could see the fungi multiply with her bare eyes, and wondered whether these furry little piles

157

of pink and white were at all comfortable in this overheated space filled with human germs. Were they happy to be watched, did they consent? And what happened after the gallery closed, who would take care of them then?

I don't understand art, her mother would've said.

At eight weeks, the woman scolded her boyfriend for leaving yellowed spinach in the fridge. Had he even read about the dangers of toxoplasmosis? In fact, had he read anything about anything at all?

"I'm doing other things for us," he replied.

"Like?" she said.

"Like this," he said, closing the fridge door the woman had left open.

For the seven years of their relationship, the woman had tried to be a good companion by replacing her tendency for competition with a more sophisticated skill: compassion. But now that she was no longer just his lover but also the mother of his child, wasn't she the one who deserved a bit more care?

That evening, the woman sat down on the sofa with her iPad and stylus. She was an illustrator and was completing a guide to root vegetables. Her work had been published in magazines over the years, even some major ones. But she was approaching thirty, and every brushstroke seemed to increase her growing sense of responsibility to do something meaningful for herself, her ancestors, whom she didn't know, and her industrious parents who had left China only to work the kind of jobs that hid them from daylight. She tasked herself with finishing up a cross-section of the beetroot. In fact, it would be the cross-section of the beetroot, after which no other cross-section would ever be needed or desired. But as soon as she opened her iPad, she found her thoughts drawn to the yellowed spinach she threw out earlier. She thought about what would've happened if she'd eaten that spinach, and perhaps, whether she should've. If she'd become sick, would her boyfriend stay home from work to take care of her? Would he bring her to bed, alongside cups of remorse and chicken soup?

The mother is a child too, her mother would've said.

At ten weeks, they bickered on their way to the doctor. Something about someone doing more than they were given credit for, something about being acknowledged and seen. It was cold and windy, the way the city never was in the movies.

"My mother would say it's bad luck to argue at the obstetrician's office," the woman told her boyfriend. "It's like fighting at weddings and funerals. You just don't do it."

"In some cultures they also consider it bad luck to mention weddings and funerals in one go," he replied, proud of his knowledge.

The nurse directed them to the exam room, where the boyfriend seemed happy to remain quiet. The woman laid in the chair, naked from the waist down, flipping through a pamphlet on urinary incontinence.

The obstetrician walked in. The woman thought she was beautiful, with smooth tanned skin and eyes somehow big and narrow at the same time.

"When did you say your last menstrual period was?" the obstetrician asked, as she inserted a probe into the woman's vagina. "July? 15th?"

"I can't believe you can see inside me with that thing," the woman said and gestured at her boyfriend to record the moment with his phone.

The woman felt she could hear the thumping of the baby's heartbeat already, even though nothing had appeared yet. To fill up the silence, the woman decided to count, silently, in cycles of ten. She wasn't sure how many cycles she had completed when the obstetrician's tanned hands started turning and poking the probe around as if she was looking for a coin that had fallen through sofa cushions. Then, she stopped.

"I'm so sorry," the obstetrician said, dimming her voice. "I don't see any signs of pregnancy."

"You...don't...?" the woman repeated slowly, as if she was worried about mispronouncing the words.

"I believe you're experiencing a case of phantom pregnancy," the doctor continued. There had been no placenta, no fetus. Nothing they could see, nothing they could hear. "It happens more often than you think. About one to six times for every 22,000 births."

The boyfriend, a man who had a retort for everything, was at a loss for words. The obstetrician turned in his direction.

"The woman usually sees the return of her period very quickly," the doctor assured him. "Her hormone levels will start dropping soon, alongside the gradual decline of—"

"But why me?" the woman asked, cutting her off.

"It could be emotional distress or a hormonal imbalance," the obstetrician said, before dimming her voice once more. "I know this can be hard, so feel free to stay in this room for as long as you want."

At home, the woman threw herself on the couch and typed "phantom pregnancy" into Google. The medical term is pseudocyesis. Hippocrates described it in 300 BC. Mary Tudor, the English queen, had it. Freud's most famous patient, "Anna O", had it. Dogs, more often than humans, have it. Women in ancient China had it, where doctors attributed the phenomenon to excessive female emotion or relations with spirits. Some women were purged, with horse tails, of the "monsters" in their bellies. Others gave birth to baby ghosts.

"Interesting," the boyfriend said.

The woman typed: "How many births per year in New York?" The answer was 120,000. If it occurred one to six times every 22,000 births, it would come down to roughly 5.45 to 32.73 women in the city who were going through the same as she was. Did they live in Chinatown, like she did? Did they live in Queens, Brooklyn, The Bronx, or Staten Island? Did they have jobs? "Real" children?

"Maybe I should say I had a miscarriage," the woman announced. She couldn't fathom explaining that all she's been carrying was a phantom, a fantasy. That her body was like one of those prank gift boxes that, once opened, turned out to contain nothing at all.

"Why would you do that?" her boyfriend said.

"Technicalities aside," the woman said, her voice trembling. "We lost a baby."

As if her body understood she needed help making her point, blood started flowing out of her seat, staining the cushions. Her boyfriend, aghast again at the mysterious workings of the female body, ran to the bathroom to get a tampon.

At what would've been eleven weeks, the woman went on a walk with her friends through Washington Square Park. It was a sunny October day that felt like European summer. Students laid on the grass, using their textbooks as pillows. Grey-haired men read on park benches. Suicidal squirrels raced across the walkways, cutting off dogs and people.

"How's it going?" B said.

The woman was offended by that question. Who in their right mind would ask a woman who'd just lost a baby how it was going?

"I'm fine," she replied.

"So you didn't actually carry a baby?" A asked.

The woman felt a ball of liquid land in her underwear. Her boyfriend had stocked their cupboards with ultra-sized tampons in the last few weeks. But she had refused to wear them, to plug up what wanted to come out.

"I know I took care of something. I loved something," she said.

"Of course," B said, placing her arm, heavy with the burden of empathy, around the woman's shoulders.

Later that evening, the boyfriend returned to find the woman lying amidst a herd of red stains on their oatmeal-colored sofa.

"Are you ok?" he asked as he ran up to her. "Should I get you a tampon?"

"B asked me how I was doing."

"She did what?"

"What does she think I've been up to all this time? Raising a hamster?"

He laid a hand on the woman's shoulder too, as if B's embrace had left an outline the boyfriend was tasked to fill.

"Why don't you focus less on what they're saying?"

"Why don't you just tell them I had a miscarriage? Do you even mind we lost a baby?"

The boyfriend sighed. He was still standing next to her, unable to find an unsoiled area on the couch.

"But how can we have lost something that was never there?"

The woman felt another splash in her underwear. Another red stain formed under her seat, gaining territory.

At what would've been twelve weeks, the woman wedged closer to the deadline for her root vegetable book. Yet, whenever she pulled out her iPad, she could only conjure soiled, cratered lumps. She had called the obstetrician's office earlier that day to ask for another ultrasound. She'd been bleeding for weeks by this point—were they certain there wasn't something more going on? But the receptionist informed her she'd have to pay her outstanding bill first—the woman's freelancer's insurance had refused to cover her previous appointment, since there had been no physical pregnancy, after all.

The doctors here prefer to wait until you've died, her mother used to say.

The woman opened her internet browser and typed phantom pregnancy into Google again, this time landing on a "phantom-babies" sub-Reddit. A husband had posted about his wife's "unproven" pregnancy, claiming it was taking a toll on their relationship and making him want to walk out on her and her "twins", quotation marks his. A woman had posted a tabloid story about another woman who, after doctors repeatedly told her she wasn't pregnant, gave birth to a healthy baby boy anyway. In the comment section below, yet another woman wrote, "Thank you for giving me hope."

Hope, the woman thought. She got up, grabbed her keys, and walked towards the subway uptown.

The train was packed for an early afternoon hour. The car seemed full, and yet managed to fill up more with every next stop. The woman held on to a pole near the door, trying to defend the square inch within her vicinity.

"Will all passengers move in-saaaaade the vehicle," a Brooklynite voice shouted through the speakers at 23rd Street. "Please. Move. IN. SADE. The vehicle."

The woman thought she heard in the sad vehicle. She moved.

"Lady! Come on!"

A man squeezed in front of her, and pushed her out of the car.

Anger swelled up in the woman, its force bloating against her skin. Would he have shoved her like that if she'd been visibly pregnant? Would the other passengers have let him? It wasn't fair that mothers only deserved esteem once their bellies were bulging out of their frames, that they only deserved a baby shower once they made it to the third trimester. That they only deserved to be seen as mothers once they'd actually produced a child.

"I'm having a miscarriage!" the woman pictured herself shouting, so loud the whole train would stare. But the train had departed already, leaving her at an emptied station.

The woman marched up Seventh Avenue. Starbucks, Taco Bell, FedEx. Red light, then green. Chase Bank, Whole Foods, Buy Buy Baby. The air was cold, her underwear wet. The woman walked into the store's fluorescent space, where she saw swollen bellies with men wandering behind them like security details. She walked past cribs and racks of jersey maternity-wear hanging under photos of smiling women in a careful assortment of skin tones. In an aisle that could only be categorized as miscellaneous hygiene items, she picked up what looked like a toy chemistry set, only to discover it was a Swedish-designed snot sucker. Since when do babies need snot suckers? Next, a plush avocado with a smiling face and a beaded stomach. A smiling popsicle with a bite taken out of its head. What the fuck were they all smiling about? The woman didn't want to be there. She didn't want to be anywhere. She felt fluids winding down her thighs like syrup dripping down a cake. She started sprinting, her feet barely gripping the vinyl.

The outside air was misty, the avenue busy. At first, she seemed to run straight into people, but as she picked up her pace, it was as if the hive-mind intelligence of the crowd was being passed down, and people further and further away started diving sideways before she even arrived. She crossed a red light and then another one, accompanied by a voice in her head telling her that one day she would die, but that today would not be the day.

Then, a crash, a break. An arm restrained her, and a heavy voice said, "Stop!"

The woman turned around and saw a security guard breathing down her neck and a trail of red down the street. He grabbed her tightly with his gloved hands, his latex fingers clasped around her humid sleeves.

"I'm having a miscarriage!" the woman shouted.

A crowd had gathered around, though she couldn't see them clearly through her blurry eyes. The guard grabbed her arms with his right hand, and pushed people aside with his left. The woman sunk into his arms, and let herself be taken away.

*   *   *

Twenty-one weeks before the positive pregnancy test. The woman's mother no longer looked like her mother. Some point down the line, all cancer patients look the same. Shriveled and immobile in their hospital beds, fed by IV's that will no longer make a difference. The woman, as the American-raised daughter, had to translate the diagnosis for certainty and clarity. As soon as her mother understood her condition, she decided to go back to China. The woman went along, because what else was a daughter supposed to do?

So there she was, her mother's skeletal frame in a bed, dressed in a checkered shirt that gave the nurses easy access to her body. The woman herself sat on a foldable bench-slash-bed in a hospital room in one of the most polluted cities in one of the most polluted countries on earth, nursing her mother's late-stage lung cancer. The woman had brought her iPad to get some work done, but all she could do was read the children's comics she found at roadside stalls, partially due to the infantile state of her Chinese. Her assignments had started to dry up anyway. The twelve-hour time difference with the United States was difficult to navigate. The censored internet even more so.

Like most other family members, the woman had taken up residence in the hospital room. There were too many patients and too few doctors, so it was the woman's job to check her mother's IV's, to feed her mother the porridge she could no longer swallow, to hold the little vials of blood they had struggled to extract from her mother's hardened arteries and to run them, five stairs down, to the lab. She had to change her mother's adult diapers too, the fullness of which her mother indicated with a pat on the bed.

A week before her mother died, even the strongest morphine couldn't subdue her incessant wailing. No matter how many times the woman asked the nurses to up her mother's dose, explaining the situation in her basic Chinese, she was inevitably met with a pair of shrugging shoulders in white coats, claiming there was nothing more they could do. Her mother's diaper now needed to be changed every hour or so, tarred with the black excrement that, according to a meddlesome aide, was the sign of an ending life. "The beginning or the end," the aide added, "it all looks the same."

The woman realized she didn't know how to comfort her mother, since they hadn't spent much time together when she was growing up. What was her mother's favorite dessert, her favorite song? Through trial and error, the woman discovered that brushing the few hairs her mother had left seemed to comfort her, if only temporarily. That gave her a sense of achievement, which was quickly followed by an itch of injustice. Her mother had never taken care of her as a child, always out working or flirting with men. As the woman wove her fingers through the barren landscape of her mother's scalp, she suddenly thought, What am I doing here, so far away from home?

Five days before her mother died, an old classmate came to visit. Her mother's demeanor temporarily improved, as the classmate talked about which of their old friends had built up businesses and which had gone through divorce. The woman stepped out of the room and wandered down the corridors, lined with empty canisters of hand sanitizer the nurses didn't have time to refill. The woman had tried to paint the scene for her white boyfriend and white friends. How the hospital's hallways were covered with clothing lines that floundered under the weight of dripping undergarments, washed by patients and family members in its bathrooms. How ludicrous it was to treat lung cancer patients in a building on a ten-lane intersection where cars, motorbikes, and bicycles sputtered gas and dust into its windows. How she didn't realize the entryway she passed every morning was the morgue until she read the handwritten note stuck on its rusty metal doors saying, This is the morgue. But none of them understood the circumstances she had to navigate, nor why her mother had chosen this decrepit place over a private New York hospital her insurance would've paid for. How could she explain that the pain you know is a friendlier land than the comfort you don't? That poverty is not just a condition but also a habit that outlasts it? The woman had long accepted that she'd have to face her mother's death, but she never anticipated it would be an experience so invisible to the loved ones she had left.

The day before the mother died, her vitals increased. Her stationary heartbeat reached the heights of a runner, her blood pressure creeping up. She was wearing an oxygen-mask, unable to speak. But her eyes followed her daughter's movements through the room. Her daughter's complexion seemed yellowed, her shoulders tense.

At this rate, she'll look fifty by the time she's thirty-two, the mother thought.

The mother wondered what her daughter saw in her now-useless body. Should she have brought her to China more, taught her better Chinese? Should she have let her go off with those American friends of hers, with whom she spent all her time? Should she have let it come this far, where her daughter now had to take care of her instead?

The child is a mother too, she thought.

It was wet. The inside of her body seemed to be leaking out. The mother mustered all her strength to move her hand up and down.

Pat.

Pat.

Pat pat.

Her daughter turned around and sat down on the wooden stool next to her bed, staring into the mother's blurry eyes. Time passed, though the mother could no longer grasp its meaning.

Pat.

Pat.

Pat pat pat. Pat pat.

Her daughter put her hand on the mothers, a grip strong and warm. The mother tried to move again, but did not succeed.

The day the mother died, the undertaker came to wrap up her body in the type of traditional clothing she'd never worn in her entire life.

"It's tradition," the undertaker informed her daughter, who looked confused.

They dressed the mother in an imitation-silk jacket and trouser set, closed with Chinese button-knots. The shiny fabric was supposed to resemble gold-thread but looked more like the reflective neon found on safety vests. They propped up her head with a square pillow and covered her dull hair with a round hat. Then, she was placed in a large body bag. As they carried her down, she saw that her checkered shirt had been thrown away in the dumpster.

Everything passes, the mother thought. Even death.

* * *

The woman woke up under bright fluorescent light. Her forehead was damp, her crotch humid.

"Am I in the hospital?"

The face of the security guard appeared. The woman was lying on the couch in Buy Buy Baby's back office. He had chased her down to make sure she was okay, and then called her emergency contact after she passed out. Her boyfriend was on his way.

"Water?" he asked.

She turned towards the wall, where she saw security monitors displaying footage from the store. Her blood blemished the sandy vinyl floors, its streaks undulating like an image of primordial life. An uniformed worker lined up yellow signs reading Caution! Wet Floor! A cleaning crew followed, dragging mops and buckets.

"They're taking it away?" the woman squealed.

"Ma'am," the security guard said, "your blood is all over baby toys."

The staff started cleaning the floor, diluting its red color like the fading light of sunset. Soon, the only visible trace of the woman's blood disappeared into the darkened liquid in their buckets.

"Actually, can I have a recording of this footage?" the woman asked. She quickly added, "I lost a baby."

Back in their apartment, the woman's body felt wet and sticky. The woman wasn't sure whether she was covered in blood, sweat, or tears, or whether there was really any difference. The boyfriend looked tired and tense, as if he was knotting up his muscles just to keep himself together.

"You should really bring more tampons next time," he said, as he turned on the kettle.

Later that night, the woman and the boyfriend laid on opposite sides of the bed, not even their hair touching. The boyfriend had fallen asleep, the woman had not. In fact, it was precisely the boyfriend's ability to sleep that was keeping the woman up. She stared at the back of his head, where each of his curls seemed ruled by a different source of gravity. His limbs were tucked into his torso, aerodynamically. The woman went to the bathroom, not because she had to pee but because she didn't know what else to do with the stretch of night that was left.

Sitting on the toilet, the woman opened her phone and played the video the guard had sent her. The footage was grainy, the cleaners looking like ghostly farmers tilling the scorched earth of the American retail landscape. The woman closed her eyes and pictured her root vegetables. She imagined how, even though their tops looked like any leafy plant, their real transformation took place underground and out of sight, as their seeds swelled up, over weeks, into corpulent, pregnant bodies. Bulbs of beetroot jumped out of the earth, their pink and luscious fruit catapulting towards the sky. Carrots leapt out of her iPad, shaking off the soil that had weighed down their ruby bodies. Potatoes rejoiced, huddling together like a nest of baby rabbits.

Pop, a splash of water. Waves started to travel through the woman, lifting her to a place of warmth. Her flesh made its way inward, as if this was the first time the woman had truly inhabited her body. If she would have had to describe this sensation to someone, she'd say it felt like taking drugs. But she had no one around her, nor did she want to. The waves came faster, their peaks higher. Sweat snaked down her back, causing her to slip back and forth. The woman didn't know what she was feeling, except that tensing all her muscles at once brought her relief. So she tightened, and tightened, and tightened, for an infinite amount of time. Suddenly, she let go, overcome by a welcome sense of emptiness.

The woman looked down and saw a round mass the size of her palm in the toilet. She quickly stuck her hand in the turbid water and picked it up, holding it up to the light. The shape was soft and pliable, settling into an embrace with the woman's fingers. Its surface was covered in a network of vessels that pulsated in symphony. The woman brought it to her face and touched it with her lips. It felt slippery and smooth, like a human turned inside out. The woman grabbed her phone and took a picture of the blob, which was quickly dissolving in her hand. It was changing, it already had.

EMILY ROTH

The Whirling Aftermath

We're crouched together under the overpass, me and Tyler, the sky blooming pond-green, the tornado sirens high-pitched and discordant, looping like a fucked up child's toy, and of course the rest of band class is here too, and the bus driver is crying, and the performance at State's went fine, not that you asked, but Tyler won't even look at me, and this is the closest we've been since I gave him a handjob at Monica's bonfire party last weekend, and he hasn't responded to any of my texts since, not the ones that were just emojis, not the ones that were, well, anyway, I can feel the wind inside my eardrums, I can feel it pummeling my body, punching me over and over, like that time in eighth grade, and we don't know yet how the world will look later, don't realize the candy shop downtown is being ripped inside out, spewing lollipops and caramels for miles, and maybe Tyler knows that I memorized his face in the firelight when he came, the way his mouth crumpled, and I'll notice his mouth do almost the same thing again when we step off the bus and see the cars flipped on their backs like beetles, the old oak snapped clean down the middle, the broken glass like a sugar-dusting over everything, and if I eat the candy I find later, even months from now, grime-crusted, shoe-stomped, but miraculously still whole, would you blame me?

RUTH MOORE

The Sofa

Aisha leans her head back and stretches her stiff legs. She can no longer state with precision where she ends and her daughter begins. These past weeks have blurred the two of them into a single being, fat with loss. Some days one of them showers, makes coffee, fetches bread. But mostly they nest together in the sofa.

It is afternoon, Aisha thinks, although today she could not persuade herself to open the curtains. She lies at the north end of the sofa, against cushions still sharp-scented with dye. Her daughter is at the south end, curled tight. Between them is a crumpled newspaper, scattered with flakes of pastry.

A neighbour brings almond croissants and the paper once a week. On Saturdays, perhaps? Yes, Saturdays. Of all the gestures of sympathy, this is one Aisha can bear to consume. She reads, for the world burns. She eats, for her husband loved too-sweet pastries. With bills biting, and ice crusting the hallways, her neighbour cannot afford such luxuries. And yet she does. And so Aisha eats, she reads, with the warmth of her daughter's ankle close against hers.

The sofa is honey yellow and soft. Her husband bought it in an online auction with his first pay cheque in this country. It was delivered the day after he died. Its generous embrace would have troubled him. He always liked to sit straight, alert for the next opportunity.

And what now, thinks Aisha, as her daughter shifts against her.

And what now?

ALLISON FIELD BELL

Carve

Been almost a decade, but I still feel him on my skin. The way his hands wrapped around my wrists, my neck. Winter in Indiana – snow thick, streets unplowed. He slammed me against a wall. Once, twice. The wall was white. I remember the texture of it: tiny irregular craters of paint that gathered dust. A voice saying, "do it, hit me." My voice. And he didn't, did he? But I still wear him there – wrapped around my wrists clattering like bangles, tight at my throat like a collar. Even though I've had a dozen men and women since him, I still walk around wounded: wrists aching, spit unswallowable. Winter in Indiana, and when I was freed from his grip, I ran outside barefoot, felt the sidewalk so cold it burned. I wanted to curl up in the snow, spread the burn all over my body. But instead, I went back inside: to him and the objects of my life. Studied the kitchen table – its red spray-painted legs. My table. From my childhood. I took a butcher knife from the drawer, and by then he was standing there in the doorway, at the threshold. Saying something sarcastic about me and the knife and the violence I could inflict with it. But I ignored him. My feet numb, I took the knife to the table and carved. One letter and then the next. My name. My table. My body, wrists, neck, skin.

RACHEL LASTRA

The Sandcastle

Eight years ago, my father was diagnosed as a sandcastle. A doctor gave him a piece of paper and a pen and asked him to draw a clock. The pen slipped through the grains of his fingers, and the paper grew damp and see-through where his wet, sandy palm rested against it. She said it was common, that there are six million sandcastles walking around in various stages of disintegration. Like this might comfort. Her hand was cool against mine.

I've been following him around with a broom and dust pan, sweeping him into colorful plastic buckets I store in the closet. When he asks where the rest of him has gone, I pull out a handful of sand and tell the story of each grain, each broken piece of shell, which beach it came from, how the tides have changed since then. Sometimes I add water and try to pack it back onto him, at an elbow or the top of his head. It never holds. The sand slides back off. I sweep him up. I close the closet.

The hospice nurse brought over a plastic kiddie pool: bright blue with orange and yellow fish. Garibaldi, my father said, before he stopped speaking. The nurse said to fill it and put my father inside, to let him settle in a layer under the water, to let him rest. She said I'll know when it's time, that I'll feel it. The pull of the moon. The ebb of the tide.

KATHLEEN LATHAM

Anna Wonders Whether Birds Will Build a Nest with Cat Hair

If they find it floating on the breeze, say. Or caught on a kalyna bush, tucked among the blood-red berries. Will they recognize the hair's softness, its capacity for warmth? Or will the scent of their enemy scare them away – a harbinger of danger unfit to be tucked into a twirl of twigs?

Anna pictures the nests she has stumbled upon, masterpieces of stems and sticks, pine needles, moss. She has heard of birds using snakeskins and spider silk, so why not cat hair, especially if the cat lies dead in a field, far from home.

Anna thinks of this as she struggles to remove the soldier's coat. As she rolls his body and tugs at his sleeves, avoiding his frozen blue gaze, dodging thoughts of his mother.

I have a boy, she whispers to him, to her. *I have a boy, and the nights are cold.*

Half a mile down the road, her son sleeps on a thin mattress, unaware she is out in this muddy field, wrestling with a dead man's coat. When it finally wrenches free, Anna brings it to her nose. Smells hatred and fear. *Who vanquished who?* she thinks proudly. Then she scrambles away, back to the tree line. She feels the weight of black bead eyes. Hears the rustling of wings. A murmur of approval.

She will go home and wash the scent of death away. Fill the coat's pockets with chamomile, oregano, poppies. Drape it across her son while he dreams.

CHRISTOPHER NOTARNICOLA

On the Nextdoor App

My neighbor says flooding would prove less problematic if trucks would stop sending waves through his doorway. Omaha Steaks have overtaken my mailbox. The bank sold my mortgage to a company called Mr. Cooper. Previous homeowners elevated my house eleven inches, and the crawlspace is littered with hand-sawed struts, concrete shims, cracked four-by-fours, rusted cans of Raid. If everyone would drive more slowly, my neighbor says. If they were conscious of their wakes. Termites swarmed for three days, making their way across the neighborhood from the east, and we blacked the windows at night like in wartime. If this is the apocalypse, my neighbor says, the book was better. Mosquitos breed in standing water. Flesh flies breed in their namesake. I broke through the floorboards to watch floodwaters knock lumber into a nook beneath the Florida room. Is it sewage, my neighbor asks, or something more sinister? The stench from our street entered uninvited. The sheen on my porch brought a great heron to feed. I haven't seen the mail truck since before the rains, and my neighbor wonders when its absence becomes illegal. How long, he asks, before they must send a boat? If a heron can stand, so can a courier. So too can a resident. Termites migrate west. Mosquitoes cloud at the sunken curb. Once more, my neighbor asks, did anyone get my Omahas by mistake? Flesh flies crawl in and out of my mailbox through gaps in the doorway. Mr. Cooper wants their money.

ADAM Z. ROBINSON

God Save the King

And he spent his seventieth year complaining about drones that drop spores on us, and not having that cough seen to. And he can't see the point of the health service that saved his late wife's life. And in his leaking loft he has three of those fancy vases (the ones that cashed-in big on the antique programme) collecting water. And in his cellar is a tub of his sons' wrestling figures and one day he'll just flog the lot of them to stop the fighting. And there's a photo somewhere that, if you hold it at the right angle in the right light, you can see his mother standing in the shadowy doorway of St Mary's, holding the bride's flowers, and if you tilt it the other way, she's gone again. And there's mould he can't shift in the gold opera glasses left to him by his father, who never used them, not once. And he doesn't remember ever having his hair that long, but here's a lock to prove it. And all of this talk about what he can't say gives him whiplash and once, when he was eleven, he was on a science programme on telly talking about seatbelt innovations and he got to go to London and he's never been back. And all he wants is to build sandcastles on the beach with his granddaughters, but he hasn't enough diesel to get him to the coast and these electric cars are a con anyway.

STEPHEN WUNDERLI

Patterns

The machinery gives her a headache, Katarina tells herself. The rolling cylinders pressing patterns of baby clothes onto thin translucent paper with cut marks and stitching lines; selvage, center front, grainline, and diamonds to indicate where the garment should take shape. An x for the button, a dotted line for alteration, all formless and flat, disjointed promises. Katarina streams the leaves onto a long steel table and trims them into squares for packaging. It's a shame to fold them she thinks. She sees them come to life, tucks construct the flared bottom, darts give the toddler's chest shape. Lightweight cotton poplin or better, twill the color of marigolds. They fill with air against the chalk-blue sky. The noise of the presses now a hum against life itself, a carotid surge. Katarina focuses on her work, cutting, folding lifeless tissue paper. No one talks in the press room. No one will try to speak her language anyway. Katarina takes her break outside. She can still hear the machinery rumbling like something approaching that will destroy the world. She will not let fear capture her. Nobody knows why a mortsafe is there in the courtyard. It's where Katarina sits and stares at the printed photograph of the little girl in the pressed cotton dress, the envelope that will hold the pattern, the instructions to piece the child together she'd lost. Katarina's eyes fill with rage and anger and hatred until she is curled up, her face flat against the iron cage.

Biographies

Judges' Biographies

Christopher Allen is the editor-in-chief and publisher of *SmokeLong Quarterly*. A teacher, editor, and translator, Allen is the author of the flash fiction collection *Other Household Toxins* (Matter Press). His work appears in *The Best Small Fictions* (Sonder Press) and *Flash Fiction America* (Norton), as well as over one hundred journals and anthologies. He and his husband are nomads but might be sighted occasionally in Munich, Germany.

Colin Barrett is from County Mayo, Ireland. His debut collection of stories, *Young Skins*, was awarded the Rooney Prize, the Frank O'Connor International Short Story Prize and the Guardian First Book Award. His stories have appeared in the *Stinging Fly*, the *New Statesman*, the *New Yorker* and *Harper's*. His second short story collection, *Homesickness*, was published in 2022. *Wild Houses*, his debut novel, will be published in 2024.

Roger Robinson is the recipient of the T.S. Eliot Prize and RSL Ondaatje Prize for *A Portable Paradise*, which was also a New Statesman Book of the Year. He has been commissioned by The National Trust, the V&A, and the National Portrait Gallery, amongst others, and is a co-founder of Malika's Poetry Kitchen and Spoke Lab. Recent collaborations include poetic responses to the paintings of Hurvin Anderson, for an artist's monograph, and with Johny Pitts, *Home Is Not A Place*, fusing poetry and photography in portrayal of and for Black Britain.

Writers' Biographies

Mara Bergman's poetry has been published widely here and abroad. Her first collection *The Tailor's Three Sons and Other New York Poems* won a *Mslexia* Poetry Pamphlet Competition and *Crossing Into Tamil Nadu* a Templar Quarterly Poetry Prize. She has since published two full collections with Arc: *The Disappearing Room* (2019) and *The Night We Were Dylan Thomas* (2021). Mara won the 2023 Plough Poetry Competition, judged by Imtiaz Dharker. An award-winning children's writer and editor, she is thrilled to have a poem highly commended by Roger Robinson in this year's Bridport Poetry Competition.

Kizziah Burton has been shortlisted for Forward Prize Best Single Poem 2023. She was Finalist for Gregory O'Donogue International Competition (2023), Third place Mslexia Poetry Prize (2022), Highly Commended Oxford Poetry Prize (2022), Judge's Prize – Magma Poetry Competition (2022/23), & The National Poetry Competition (2021). Second Place Ledbury Poetry Competition (2020), Shortlisted for The Bridport Prize (2022) & Aesthetica Creative Writing Award (2023). Awarded grants from the American Academy of Motion Pictures Arts & Sciences Foundation while a graduate fellow of the University of Southern California, she holds a BA in Art History/Religion with an MA in creative writing.

georgia campbell is from Stroud and graduated from UEA's Creative Writing MA in 2022. She has written a novel about an obsessive actress, and her story *digestible* has formed the grounds for another novel, this time set behind the scenes of a theatre rather than on the stage. She used to be a tutor and now works as a transcription editor.

Andrew De Silva was raised in metro Detroit and studied fiction at the University of Southern California, where he is now an associate professor in the University's undergraduate writing program. His fiction debuted in the *Missouri Review* in 2018 and has since won *december* magazine's Curt Johnson Prose Award and *Bayou Magazine*'s James Knudsen Prize for Fiction. He lives in Los Angeles, California with his wife and two young children. This story is drawn from his recently completed novel manuscript *Journeyman*, set in the world of professional tennis.

Mustapha Enesi is a short story writer whose works explore minority voices and complex familial relationships. In 2021, he won the K&L Prize for African Literature with a story about a young girl who develops severe mental health issues. In the same year, he won the Awele Creative Short Story Prize with a story about a woman who, after seven miscarriages in seven years of marriage, decided to remove her womb as a way to seek agency from the toxic clutches of patriarchy; it was later published in Harvard's Transition Magazine. He is Ebira, and he writes from Lagos, Nigeria.

Allison Field Bell is originally from northern California but has spent most of her adult life in the desert. She is currently pursuing her PhD in Prose at the University of Utah, and she has an MFA in Fiction from New Mexico State University. Her prose appears in *SmokeLong Quarterly*, *The Gettysburg Review*, *Shenandoah*, *New Orleans Review*, *West Branch*, *Epiphany*, *Alaska Quarterly Review*, *The Pinch*, and elsewhere. Her poems appear or are forthcoming in *The Cincinnati Review, South Dakota Review, Sugar House Review, The Greensboro Review, Nimrod International Journal,* and elsewhere. Find her at allisonfieldbell.com.

Asia Haut lives in Kent with her husband and son. She studied History of Art at The University of Manchester and taught the subject for a number of years, though she now works with undergraduate students with disabilities. Her first piece of published fiction appeared in *Mslexia* in 2022. She is currently writing more short stories and working on a novel.

Alyson Kissner is co-winner of the 2022 Edwin Morgan Poetry Award for Scottish-based poets under 30. She has also been shortlisted for the 2022 Rebecca Swift Foundation Women Poets' Prize and the 2023 Scottish Book Trust New Writers Award. Originally from Vancouver, Canada, Alyson is completing her PhD in Creative Writing at the University of Edinburgh. Her creative and critical practices interrogate themes of identity/memory, mythmaking, grief, power, and the natural world, as well as the ways abuse functions in personal relationships. Her work can be found at alysonkissner.com.

Lance Larsen is the author of five poetry collections, most recently *What the Body Knows* (Tampa 2018). His poems have appeared in *London Magazine, The Times Literary Supplement, Paris Review, New York Review of Books, Poetry Wales, New England Review*, and *Best American Poetry 2009*. His awards include a Pushcart Prize and a fellowship from the National Endowment for the Arts. He teaches at Brigham Young University and likes to fool around with aphorisms: "A woman needs a man the way a manatee needs a glockenspiel." In 2017 he completed a five-year appointment as Utah's poet laureate.

Rachel Lastra is a writer and editor currently based in the Pacific Northwest. Her fiction has been published in *Barrelhouse, Smokelong Quarterly, Apparition Lit, Chestnut Review,* and *MoonPark Review,* and she was a finalist in the 2023 Flash Frog flash fiction contest. She is a student in the MA in writing program at Johns Hopkins University and is currently at work on a novel. Find her at www.rachellastra.com.

Kathleen Latham is a poet and writer living outside of Boston, Massachusetts. Twice nominated for *The Best Small Fictions,* she's won the Web Microfiction Prize for Women Writers, *Writer's Digest's* Short Short Story Competition, and placed third in Bath Flash Fiction. Her work has been shortlisted for the First Pages Prize, Welkin Writing Prize, Fish Flash Fiction, *Fractured Lit,* and *New Flash Fiction Review.* Her work has appeared or is forthcoming in such places as *Reflex Fiction, The Masters Review,* and *Fictive Dream.* She tweets from @lathamwithapen and can be found online at KathleenLatham.com.

Alex Luke is a writer from London. She has an MFA in fiction from Rutgers University-Camden, where she was the recipient of an Interdisciplinary Fellowship. Her short fiction has been published in The *Good Journal* and *SAND* Journal. She's been nominated for a Pushcart Prize, and the STACK Awards. She is a nanny and a bookseller, and she's currently working on her first novel. Find her on Twitter at @alexjaneluke

Fred Lunzer is a writer coming out of the tech world, his day job is in AI research and strategy. He has British and German citizenship, grew up in London and Tokyo, and speaks Japanese. He is the third of five children, and his family is made up of writers, musicians, jewellers and filmmakers. His debut novel, *SIKE,* will be published by Celadon.

Tom Miles lives in London and supplements his negligible writing income by selling doorknobs and tennis rackets. He is the proud father of two daughters and the rather less proud author of two novels and two collections of shorter fiction. Two of his stories for children have been adapted for television and broadcast by BBC Persian. He has two bad knees and no real interest in numerology. Tom researches and writes on James Joyce, violence in art, and the weather. He struggles with comma usage and talking sensibly about himself in the third person. He remains optimistic.

Ruth Moore writes fiction and poetry for all ages. Her as-yet unpublished novel *The Enemy Inside* won the Bath Children's Novel Award (2020). Before success in 2023, her flash fiction was shortlisted for the Bridport Prize (2021) and her story 'Homecoming' was highly commended in the 2022 Historical Writers' Association short fiction awards. She is represented by Stephanie Thwaites at Curtis Brown. After a first career in theatre, creative education, and project management, Ruth is embarking on a PhD at Exeter University. Her research focuses on the possibilities and problematics of exploring silenced (hi)stories through children's time-slip fiction. Instagram: @ruthmoorewrites

Mary Mulholland's poems are published in many journals including *bath magg*, *14 Magazine*, *Aesthetica*, *Under the Radar*, *Rialto*, *Finished Creatures*, *Stand*, and in anthologies by Candlestick Press and Corrupted Poets among others. This year she's been longlisted in the National Poetry Prize, Rialto Nature & Place, placed in Wolves, Teignmouth, and commended / shortlisted in Ver, Ware, Fish, Plough, Bedford andSouth Downs. She has a pamphlet, *What the sheep taught me* (Live Canon, 2022) and two collaborations with Simon Maddrell and Vasiliki Albedo (Nine Pens). She founded the platform Red Door Poets and co-edits *The Alchemy Spoon*.

Christopher Notarnicola's work has appeared in *AGNI*, *American Short Fiction*, *Bellevue Literary Review*, *Best American Essays*, *Best Microfiction*, *Chicago Quarterly Review*, *Image*, *River Teeth*, *The Southampton Review* and other publications. Find him in Fort Lauderdale, Florida and at christophernotarnicola.com.

Jean O'Brien's 6th collection *Stars Burn Regardless* was published by Salmon Publishing in 2022. She is widely published and has received prizes and awards, including winning the Arvon International, the Fish International and been placed/runner up in others such as the Forward Prize (Single Poem). She was Poet in Residence in the Irish Cultural Centre in Paris in 2021 and awarded a Patrick Kavanagh Fellowship in 2017/18. She received an M. Phil in creative writing/poetry from Trinity College Dublin and has taught in places as diverse as community centres, schools, prisons, the Irish Writers Centre and at post graduate level.

Erin O'Luanaigh received her MFA from the University of Florida. Her poems have appeared in *The Yale Review, Bad Lilies, AGNI, 32 Poems, The Southern Review, Subtropics,* and *The Hopkins Review,* among other journals. Originally from Connecticut, she currently lives in Salt Lake City, Utah, where she is a PhD candidate in poetry at the University of Utah and cohost of the film and literature podcast, *(sub)Text.*

Eamon O'Riordan lives in Greenwood, Ontario, with his wife Melissa. His writing has appeared in *The Antigonish Review, The Honest Ulsterman* and *The Galway Review.* He is currently working on a collection of short stories.

Jenny Pagdin's pamphlet *Caldbeck,* was published by Eyewear in 2017 and shortlisted for the Mslexia pamphlet competition. Competition wins include second prize in the Café Writers competition 2021, Café Writers Norfolk prize 2017 and longlisting in the Rebecca Swift Foundation Women's Poetry Prize 2018. Her work is featured or forthcoming in *New Welsh Review, Smoke, Magma, Ambit, The Stand, Wild Court, Finished Creatures, Ink, Sweat & Tears, Interpreter's House* and an Emma Press anthology. She was born into an English-Lebanese family and lives in Norwich with her husband and child, where she works as a fundraiser in the voluntary sector.

Amanda Quaid is a writer, performer, and multi-disciplinary artist in New York. Plays include *The Extinctionist, The Clam, Echo and Narcissus,* and *Circumstances Affecting the Heat of the Sun's Rays.* Her first opera libretto will premiere with Heartbeat Opera in 2024. As a filmmaker, Ms. Quaid received a LUNAFEST prize for her short, *Toys,* which she adapted, directed, and hand-animated. The film was also honored with a Best Animation prize at DC Shorts. She began writing poetry in 2023, and her work has been published in *Rattle.* She is a graduate of Vassar College.

Margaret Ray grew up in Gainesville, Florida. She is the author of *GOOD GRIEF, THE GROUND* (BOA Editions, 2023, winner of the A. Poulin Jr. Poetry Prize selected by Stephanie Burt) and the chapbook *SUPERSTI-TIONS OF THE MID-ATLANTIC* (2022, selected by Jericho Brown for the 2020 Poetry Society of America Chapbook Fellowship Prize). Her poems have appeared in *The Atlantic, Best New Poets 2021, Threepenny Review, Narrative,* and elsewhere. A shortlister for the Montreal International Poetry Prize, she teaches in New Jersey. She's on Twitter & BlueSky @mbrrray, on Instagram @m_rrray. You can find more of her work at www.margaretbray.com

Adam Z. Robinson is a writer and theatre-maker. His work includes: *Upon the Stair* ("Everyone needs to see this show" – The Reviews Hub) and *Smile Club* (★★★★ The Guardian) co-written with Andrea Heaton. His plays *The Book of Darkness & Light* and *Shivers* toured nationally between 2016-2019. Adam has adapted classic works for the stage: *Haunted* (two national tours, 2023) and *A Christmas Carol* (national tours 2019-21, residency at Barons Court Theatre, London, 2022, forthcoming residency at Saint John Theatre Company, New Brunswick, Canada, 2023). Adam's other writing includes: *Conscientious* (national tour 2014) and *Seaside Terror* (national tours 2017-20) with OddDoll Theatre.

Emily Roth is a librarian and writer. She was the first place winner of Reflex Fiction's Winter 2022 flash fiction competition, and her writing has also been published by *SmokeLong Quarterly*, *The Masters Review*, *Exposition Review*, and others. She lives in Chicago with her rescue dog, Obie.

Joyce Schmid's poems have appeared in *New Ohio Review, The Hudson Review, Five Points, Literary Imagination,* and other journals and anthologies. She lives with her husband of over half a century in Palo Alto, California, USA.

Joelle Schumacher is a poet, painter, printmaker, and photographer. They currently reside in Denver, Colorado, where they teach weekly poetry workshops and miss quality public transportation.

Mohini Singh studied Computer Science at Cambridge and worked as a software engineer for eight years before deciding it was not the career for her. She took evening classes in creative writing at City Lit and completed a diploma in Novel Writing from Birkbeck. Her short stories have been published in *Long Story*, *Short*, *The Wrong Quarterly* and *The Good Journal*. She's recently completed her first novel and is currently working on her second. In her free time she learns Japanese and does voluntary tutoring in English and Maths.

Radhika Maira Tabrez is a writer, editor, L&D specialist, TEDx speaker, and radio show host. Her debut novel *In The Light Of Darkness* won the much-coveted *Muse India* – Satish Verma Young Writer Award in 2016. Radhika's stories and essays have appeared in many anthologies and magazines since then. In 2018, she became the first Indian ever to speak at a TEDx event in Bangladesh. She has won the *Rising Stars India Award*

(2017), and *100 Most Inspiring Writers by Indian Awaaz (2018)*. She was a Program Mentor for the *Chevening Writers Series* held in Malaysia in 2020.

Danny Thiemann Venegas, an attorney at Earthjustice, is a recipient of the 2021 Nelligan Prize for Fiction for his story 'One Bad Night in San Jose, Costa Rica', the 2020 Tobias Wolff Award for Fiction for 'Echo-location for Mixed Race Runaways', a Table4 Foundation New Writer Award for 'Gotham, Mexico', a Madalyn Lamont Award for fiction from the American University in Cairo, and his story 'Our Bodies Are in the Clouds Above Their Cities' was a finalist for the 2023 Kurt Vonnegut prize. He has published in *McSweeney's Internet Tendency*, the *New Delta Review*, *Bosque Magazine*, the *Idaho Review*, and elsewhere.

Shane Tivenan is an Irish writer, currently based in Madrid. His work has appeared in The Stinging Fly, The London Magazine, and has been broadcast on RTÉ Radio 1. In 2020 he won the RTÉ Francis MacManus Award for 'Flower Wild', a short story about Violet Gibson, the Irish woman who shot Mussolini in the nose.

Mary Wang is a writer and editor based in New York. Her work has been featured in BOMB, the Guardian, Michigan Quarterly Review, New York Public Radio, Vestoj, and Vogue, among others. She was a 2021-2022 Emerging Writers Fellow at the Center for Fiction and a senior editor at Guernica. At the latter, she founded and led *Miscellaneous Files*, a series of virtual studio visits that used writers' digital artifacts to understand their practice.

Stephen Wunderli is a writer living in Utah. He has published work in *The Kalahari Review*, *Grub Street Literary Magazine*, and *The Dawn Review*. He grew up idolizing cowboys, riding motorcycles and hoping the world wouldn't end before he'd run out of stories. So far so good.

William Wyld is a gender non-conforming poet and visual artist from South London. Costume and identity are central to their writing and performing, which is rooted in nature and the landscape, relating to their practice as a painter. William has performed at the Poetry Library, Wilderness festival, Wandsworth Fringe and featured at poetry nights around London. They have been published in *Lighthouse*, *Queer Life Queer Love II*, *the Live Canon sonnet anthology 154*, and exhibited at the Royal Academy Summer Show and Discerning Eye exhibitions. A carpenter by trade, William recently helped rebuild the Museum of Childhood in Bethnal Green.